# MODELS FOR
# EXPERIMENTS IN PHYSICS

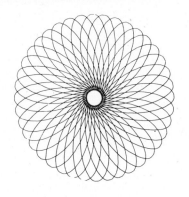

# Models
# for Experiments
# in Physics

## BY A. D. BULMAN

ILLUSTRATED

*Thomas Y. Crowell Company, New York*

# CONTENTS

# Contents

## Note

The experiments and models in this book are all interesting, and they can be great fun to perform. Your work will be easier if you make a habit of always reading thoroughly, before you begin, the experiment you wish to do. This will give you a good idea of what to expect, how much work room you will need, and what equipment is required. Assemble the equipment and each part the instructions call for. Nothing is more frustrating than reaching the midpoint of an experiment and finding that you need a special nut or bolt after the stores have closed.

Some of the experiments in this book require the use of electricity, power tools, and acids, which if not handled properly can cause serious accidents. Strict attention should be paid to the warnings you will find in each chapter in which these items are used.

# MODELS FOR
# EXPERIMENTS IN PHYSICS

# 1 A BIMETALLIC THERMOSTAT

A device that maintains a steady, or static, temperature is often referred to as a thermostat. You may be familiar with such a device in connection with a gas stove, an electric iron, or the heating system in your home. Several methods can be adopted to achieve uniform heat; but in all of them a change in shape or size of some element is made to operate a switch or tap, thereby cutting off the heat supply when the temperature has risen to some preselected level.

The vital part of the bimetallic thermostat is a strip consisting of two narrow pieces of metal of different expansibility welded or riveted together along their

*1*

length. When heated, an originally straight strip bends, as one would expect, so that the metal piece of greater expansion forms the outside of the curve. If the pieces were fixed only at the ends, an open loop would result from the heating. There is a commercially made bimetallic strip which may be bought in small lengths. It consists of a very expansible metal (such as brass) coupled with an alloy, called invar, of negligible expansibility. This large difference in expansibility results in very considerable bending. Indeed, little spiral coils of such compound strip are used in one type of thermometer. One end of the spiral is fixed; the other carries a pointer which rotates around a temperature-graduated dial.

It is not difficult, however, to make a compound strip from the readily obtainable metals iron and aluminum, which exhibit a considerable difference in expansibility. In fact, the coefficient of linear expansion of aluminum, 0.000026, is more than twice that of iron, 0.000012. That is to say, each centimeter of aluminum lengthens by 0.000026 cm. for each centigrade degree that it rises in temperature.

Similarly, of course, 1 ft. would lengthen by 0.000026 ft.; or in the case of iron, 1 ft. would lengthen by 0.000012 ft. Looked at more precisely, the increase in an aluminum strip, which would be 0.0026 ft. for each 100° C. rise in temperature, is a mere third of one-tenth of an inch and would be scarcely noticeable to the casual observer without some magnifying aid. But a *compound* strip even two or three inches long shows a visible curvature when raised 100° C. or so.

The model may be designed for either house current (110 volt) use or for a low-voltage source. Let us assume first that a 12-volt supply is available, either a.c. from a transformer or d.c. from storage batteries or a battery charger. We shall begin with the construction of the vital bimetallic strip.

Cut a length of 1-mm.-thick aluminum ½ in. wide by 4 in. long, and a similar-width strip of iron (tin can) 5 in. long. Bend the ends of the iron around the aluminum strip as shown in Fig. 1A and drill five evenly spaced holes the size of aluminum (or other soft metal) rivets. The end hole is not riveted but is intended to take a clamping screw. Two inches of the compound strip so made is sandwiched between strips of insulator, such as thin mica, asbestos paper, or any resinous sheet insulator which will not char with heat. Around this bind 10 to 12 in. of gauge 29 Nichrome wire, which will constitute the main heating element in the apparatus.

The dimensions of the containing box are a matter of personal choice, but the size of the writer's model is indicated in Fig. 1B. The lower end of the compound strip *F* is screwed down rigidly to the side of the box but separated from it by a metal spacer block ½ in. thick, *G*. A heavy washer or large nut, *H*, under the

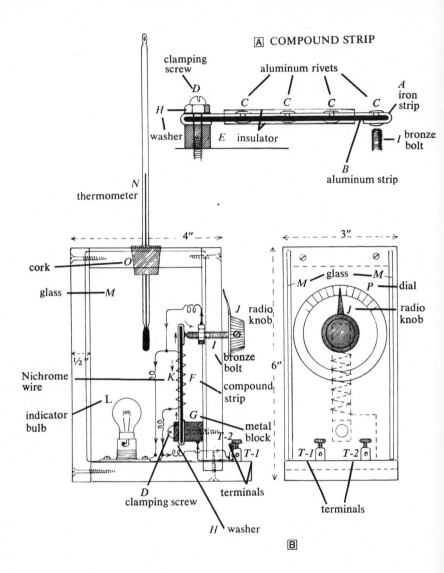

Fig. 1 The bimetallic thermostat

screw head completes the rigid clamping of this end of the compound strip, which is fitted with its aluminum face toward the side of the box. A bronze bolt *I* about 1½ in. long is screwed tightly through a hole of correct size in the side framework so that it can make contact with the bimetallic strip near its free end; that is, it makes electrical contact with the aluminum side. A radio knob and pointer *J* may be fitted to the screw so that it can serve as an adjusting knob. The pointer will move around a dial *K*, which will later be graduated in degrees of temperature.

The indicator bulb *L*, a 12-volt car headlight bulb, is held in a socket on the base and is wired in parallel with the heater wire already mentioned. From Fig. 1B it will be seen that current enters terminal *T-1* and goes through the compound strip, through the control screw which is joined to the Nichrome heater and indicator bulb, and from there to *T-2*. When the temperature of the heater has risen, the strip will curve and break contact with the tip of the control screw. It will then cool down, remake contact, and a further period of heating will ensue. The more the control screw is turned clockwise, the longer the period of heating before the contact breaks. Obviously, clockwise turning of the screw results in a higher average temperature. The whole system may be enclosed by sliding glass *M* into suitable slots in the back and front of the side framework. A thermometer will indicate the mean temperature at which the box remains thermostatically, and the dial on the side of the frame should be graduated in accordance with this. A very rapid rate of flashing of the bulb is maintained when the tip of the control screw just touches the compound strip. In long spells of operation, trouble will probably arise from oxidation of the contact points. Arcing across these points can be minimized by connecting a 0.05-mfd. capacitor (150 volt) across the gap. For prolonged use, however, face the contacts with suitable metal, such as tiny pieces of platinum or the cheap soft alloy substitute called platinoid.

For operation from house current the appropriate alterations are simply made. In place of the Nichrome wire an electric-iron replacement element may be fitted, and the indicator lamp may be an ordinary low-wattage light bulb. Extra care with safe insulation and grounding of exposed metal parts is obviously essential.

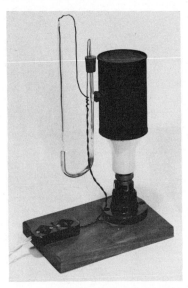

## 2 AN AIR-EXPANSION THERMOSTAT

To maintain a steady temperature, this device uses air expanded with heat, to operate a form of mercury switch.

In Fig. 2A, *A* is an inverted tin can and *B* is an ordinary light bulb. *A*, an airtight can of suitable size from which the top has been cleanly removed with a rotary can opener, is pressed onto the top of the light bulb and neatly sealed in position with epoxy glue. Rubbery adhesives were found unsuitable for this purpose, since with the heat of the bulb they lost their effect and very quickly leaked air. A hole cut in the side at *C* takes a bored cork or rubber stopper car-

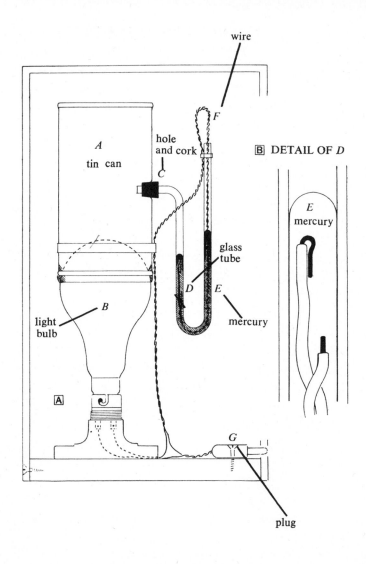

wire

A
tin can

hole
and cork
C

F

B DETAIL OF D

glass
tube

D E

E
mercury

light
bulb

B

mercury

A

G

plug

*Fig. 2 Thermostat-flasher*

rying a glass tube bent as shown. This U-tube contains a little mercury in the bend *DE*. A piece of twin plastic-covered wire *F* has been pushed around the bend to such a distance that the bared ends are just below the mercury surface at *D*. The method of exposing the bare wire ends, one above the other, is shown in Fig. 2B. One of these twin wires is joined to the electric plug *G* and the other to the lamp *B*. The second wire in the lamp is connected to *G* so that when the current is turned on, it passes through the mercury at *D*, and the lamp lights up. The lamp also rapidly heats and expands the air in the can *A*. Assuming that the apparatus has successfully been made air-tight, this expansion forces down the mercury in the limb *D*. Now the mercury contact between the wires is broken and the lamp is extinguished, so that the air cools down and contracts. After some time the mercury is pulled back from *E* to *D* and remakes the contact. Thus an average temperature is maintained by the apparatus dependent on the length of time the bulb remains lighted. This in turn depends on the depth of the bare wire ends below the mercury surface at *D*. Clearly this depth can be adjusted by pushing the loop *F* up or down to give any required rate of flashing and therefore controls the mean temperature of the thermostat.

The air trapped in the can expands about $\frac{1}{273}$ or 0.00366 (the coefficient of volume expansion of all dry gases) of its volume at 0° C. for each 1° C. rise in temperature, but it is not possible to state a precise figure for this. There are three precise laws regarding the behavior of air. One, however, requires the pressure to be constant: Charles' Law, which states the proportionality of volume and temperature. The second, the Pressure Law, requires the volume to be constant and then states the proportionality of pressure and temperature. The third, Boyle's Law, examines the inverse relationship between the pressure and volume of air at a constant temperature. Now if we think about the air trapped by the mercury in the U-tube, we see that none of these conditions strictly applies to the air in our model. As soon as the mercury moves around, its difference in level measures an increase in the pressure above atmospheric and the temperature varies as the bulb goes on and off. Clearly, the volume has increased and the air has grown warmer; thus the basic requirements of none of the individual laws are met. The fractional expansion is, however, very nearly $\frac{1}{273}$ per centigrade degree.

Temperature-control devices such as those described can be used in biological work—for example, to maintain the temperature level of animal housing in the laboratory. Boxes and tanks may be kept at one temperature. In one instance locusts were bred over long periods for research work on genetics with the right temperature maintained in their container. Similarly, incubation of eggs becomes possible with a thermostat-controlled incubator. Thermostats coupled with fans and stirrers are devices very familiar to physical chemists as well as biologists; but their widest application is in the home, where many instances of controlled heating occur.

## 3 THE SCHEMAGRAPH

Because the schemagraph will automatically draw an infinite variety of shapes, as planned by the operator, the name of this model is derived from the Greek roots *schema*, meaning a form or shape, and *graphein*, to write. The designs drawn, which might then be called schemagrams, are possibly of greater interest to the artist than to the physicist. The scientist is likely to make comparisons with Lissajous' figures as elaborated on a harmonograph, whereas the artist may be intrigued by the pattern-building repetition of trefoil, quatrefoil, and so on. In any case, the categories of physicist and artist are not mutually exclusive!

*12*

The main justification for inclusion of this model lies in the practice which its making affords in the use of the lathe and other tools. Lathe attachments for power drills are not terribly expensive, and the physicist adept in lathe technique has an advantage in being to that extent independent of the laboratory technician.

## GEARS AND CONSTRUCTION
## OF THE CONTINUOUSLY
## VARIABLE GEAR

A gear is a device whereby a drive wheel rotates another wheel at a different speed. A fact familiar to everyone who has used a bicycle is that the large gear wheel on the pedals drives the rear-wheel sprocket at a faster rate. Car gears are arranged to do the reverse —that is, to step down the fast speed of the engine to the slower speed of the rear axle. A variety of ratios is obtained by using sprocket wheels of different sizes, but the number is usually limited to three or four. Fig. 3A is included for the sake of clarity.

Where considerable reduction of speed is required it is customary either to use a succession of pinions and gear wheels or to use a worm and gear. Model railroad engines use worm and gear devices for the reduction of the high speed of the electric motor to the much slower speed of the wheels. The device is illustrated in Fig. 3B, and it will be seen that each

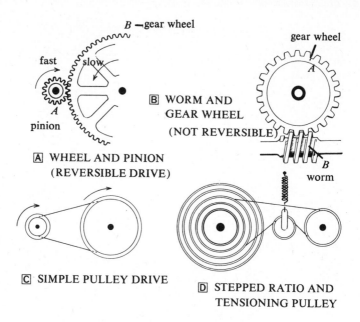

B —gear wheel

fast slow

pinion

A

B —gear wheel

**A** WHEEL AND PINION
(REVERSIBLE DRIVE)

gear wheel

A

**B** WORM AND
GEAR WHEEL
(NOT REVERSIBLE)

B
worm

**C** SIMPLE PULLEY DRIVE

**D** STEPPED RATIO AND
TENSIONING PULLEY

*Fig. 3 Speed change using gears*

turn of the worm moves the gear wheel one tooth; that is, the ratio of reduction is the number of teeth on this wheel. On small scale models one may use grooved pulleys and belts (Fig. 3C) for the purpose and so avoid the use of gear teeth. A twisted belt reverses the direction of rotation. Use of a stepped pulley would give a choice of different diameters for different gear ratios. As the length of belt needed would in this case vary, the slack could be taken up by a spring-anchored pulley (Fig. 3D), but this is scarcely necessary for small variations in length, where a spiral spring belt could replace a nonextensible one. Such flexible spring belts are often used for driving the reels of film projectors. The spring is of lighter gauge than the familiar older type of curtain-support spring available in the dime stores. This bare steel curtain spring might, in fact, be used in the present model.

The schemagraph construction requires not just a series of fixed, stepped ratios, but one that is continuously adjustable. The vital component, described first, is the variable-diameter pulley wheel.

To make axles for this and other parts of the assembly, obtain from a hardware store a length of about 18 in. of ¼ -in. threaded steel rod with half a dozen nuts and washers to match. Failing this, fine-thread brass rod, not thinner than ¼ in., could be used, but the steel rod is better in giving the necessary rigidity.

The wooden boss ($Q$ in Fig. 4) is turned on the lathe from a large cotton spool so as to have a slight taper. The wooden spool is first centralized and tightened on a piece of threaded rod and clamped in a lathe chuck. When turning, avoid over-deep cutting and biting into the wood by any attempt to cut too rapidly with the chisel. This can easily happen with the soft wood used for spools, especially if the cutting edge is blunt or not correctly positioned during turning. Get a good smooth finish by sandpapering the work in the lathe.

Obtain an old alarm clock mainspring about ¼ in.

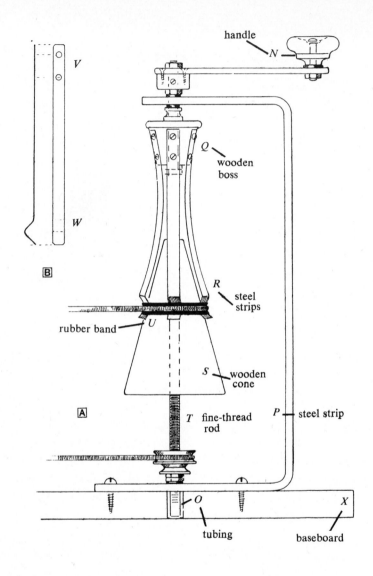

*Fig. 4 The variable-gear device*

wide. Straighten the spring and then snap off six 6-in. lengths. Soften 1 in. at both ends of each piece by holding the strips in a Bunsen flame until red-hot. Color changes quickly indicate the length from which the temper has been taken out. Fig. 4B shows the shape and comparative size of the six identical pieces required. The holes at *V* are first marked with a center punch and then drilled to take small round-head (3⁄8 in.) wood screws. All the ends *W* are bent into a V-shape; check carefully that the springs are similar in length and form. The indented ends are to clasp a smooth wooden cone, *S* (Fig. 4A).

Six lines are drawn, evenly spaced, down the side of the tapered wooden boss, and after pilot holes have been accurately marked out and drilled, the springs are screwed on.

Next, the cone mentioned, *S*, is turned from any close-grained wooden cylinder either screwed to the face plate of a lathe or held in the step chuck. The size and slope of the cone are not critical, but in a length of 3 in. it may increase from 1⁄2-in. diameter at the small end to 2 1⁄2 in. at the widest. While the cone is still mounted in the lathe, fix a twist drill in the tail-stock and run an accurately centered hole through it. This hole should be very slightly smaller than the steel rod *T* which will form its spindle. If the end of this rod is grooved longitudinally with a triangular file it may itself be used as a tap to cut its own thread in the wooden cone. The cone can then be screwed along $T$, friction-tight, inside the springs. The V-shaped ends will hold the pulley belt to a particular diameter of the cone, and this effective diameter can be made continuously variable by screwing the conical core along the spindle.

When, as suggested, spiral curtain spring was used as a pulley belt, this was found to run more smoothly and silently on the springs when a ¼-in. rubber band $U$ (cut from a bicycle inner tube) was overlaid in the V-groove.

The handle $N$ was simply made from a strip of Masonite and a knob turned from another spool, which rotated easily on a suitable axle bolt. All parts intended to be rigid with the spindle, such as the handle, spring boss, and pulleys, require some positive fixing, such as clamping lock nuts or grub screws, to avoid the possibility of slipping. Short lengths of tubing, $O$, slipped onto the threaded shaft allow it to turn freely in its bearings. The rigid mounting of the unit and its bearings takes the form of a single strip of mild steel, $P$, 1 in. wide and ³⁄₁₆ in. thick, bent and drilled for the shaft and firmly screwed down to the baseboard.

## THE PAPER CARRIER
In the machine constructed (see Figs. 5 and 6) the turntable was made from a sheet of ¼-in. fiberboard,

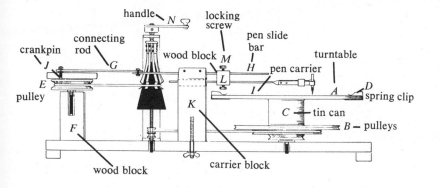

*Fig. 5 The schemagraph (elevation)*

the kind often used for bulletin boards. Quarter-inch plywood would serve equally well. A circle of 12-in. diameter was cut out with compass scribers, starting from both sides of the board, and the edge was finally smoothed out with sandpaper while the board was running in the lathe.

Beneath the paper carrier were two or three large diameter pulleys, *B*, also made from ¼-in. fiberboard by cutting circles and then turning V-grooves in the edges. The pulleys were bolted together on ¼-in. brass rod which, with the thread rubbed down, projected downward into a steel tube in the baseboard. This constituted the whole bearing. The top pulley had a centralized tin can *C* glued to it, and the paper-carrying disk was in turn glued to the top of the can. Thus it was built up to the requisite height for the pen to draw without being dragged out of the vertical by friction. It is important that the paper revolve flat under the moving pen, so check that the turntable rotates perfectly on its lower bearing. Ordinary drawing-board spring clips *D* were used to hold the paper to the board, and a double thickness of paper was sometimes found advantageous.

## THE ECCENTRIC CARRIER

Two ½-in.-thick wooden wheels were glued together. For these and other pulleys you may be lucky enough to find a hobby shop that sells toy wheels. This saves some labor in preliminary cutting, but they still have to be trued up in the lathe and V-grooves turned in their edges. The lower, 3-in. wheel *E* was cut with a V-groove to form a pulley while the upper, 4-in. one *J* was drilled to take the crankpin. For this purpose $\frac{3}{16}$-in. holes were drilled around a volute so as to give a choice of radial throw to the pin (see Fig. 6). An alternative to the spiral line of holes is to drill them along a straight wooden bar attached diametrically on top of the pulley wheel, but the volute allows them to be set more closely. If the holes are numbered for reference, this is helpful in redrawing the same design. Like other rotating units in the model, the single bearing was ¼-inch brass running in tubing mounted on a block of wood *F* (Fig. 5) screwed to the baseboard. The block was of such height as to make this pulley level with the steel-spring pulley on the cone.

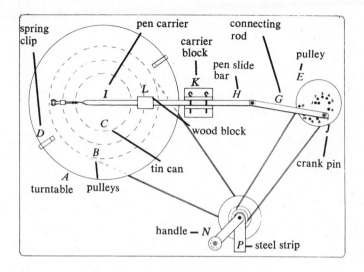

*Fig. 6 The schemagraph (plan)*

As all the speeds in the model were low, graphite grease was used in preference to oil at the various bearings.

## THE PEN-CARRIER BAR

For this, one may use three lengths of flat brass curtain rods, *G*, *H*, and *I* in Figs. 5 and 6. The piece *G* is a connecting rod with a short vertical bolt *J* screwed through a hole at one end. The bolt has part of its thread turned off to form a smooth ³⁄₁₆-in. pin. This is located in any one of the holes mentioned previously; it acts as a crankpin or eccentric, giving reciprocating motion to the pen slide bar *H*. The other end of *G* is jointed to *H* with a nut, bolt, and washers, the bolt riveted over to the extent of making the hinge free and smooth when oiled, but without play. It is a mistake to reduce the length of the bar *G* with the idea of making a more compact apparatus, since a short piece giving a wide-angle pull on *H* will make this slider seize or chatter in its groove.

Strip *H* is intended to follow a straight to-and-fro path, and no lateral play is permissible, since this would be exaggerated when transmitted to the pen. *H* is therefore made to slide smoothly but freely in a channel cut in the top of the carrier block *K*. Cutting the groove of exact width and parallel right to its end is not easy but will repay care spent on it. Using the rail *H,* mark the width of the groove with a sharp knife and with a fine hacksaw make the vertical cuts inside the lines. Then chisel out the channel and trim it with a file until the rail slides smoothly. Finally, rub in graphite and burnish it with the slider itself. Two cross pins above the rail prevent it from rising but are simply withdrawn when its removal is desired. The slide action works well if smoothed by lining the channel with thin felt; an alternative would be to cut end plates of polyethylene. This would ensure a perfect fit with very little friction.

Bolt block *K* to the baseboard by one central bolt and wing nut so that it is capable of rotation and of being clamped obliquely to the turntable.

Strip *I*, the pen carrier, should be extensible on *H*.

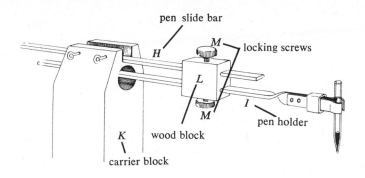

*Fig. 7 Schemagraph slider and pen holder*

Clamp *H* and *I* by means of a block of wood (*L* in Fig. 7) with two slots cut through it as shown. The slots may be cut by drilling holes subsequently linked with a wire file. A vertical hole drilled right through the block can be tapped to take the two locking screws *M*.

The pen-carrying end of *I* should be given a right-angled twist and a more springy strip of brass riveted on. This clamps the pen in position when a metal ring is pushed along it and ensures the desirable quick release coupled with rigid vertical clamping of the pen.

The nib must write smoothly in all directions, and India ink, while giving the best black line, is inclined to dry too rapidly on the nib. The most satisfactory pens were homemade glass ones. The method, in brief, was to draw out ¼-in. glass tubing, seal the sharp tip, and then rub this down on the oilstone until it was just perforated and smoothed. These pens require care in freeing the tip from drying ink, in cleansing, and in storage, but the line is fine, black, and dependable. For trial runs a ball-point pen is suitable. No special weighting of the pen was needed to give correct pressure, since the slide bar was springy and the pen depth was easily set, but blackness of line could also be increased with a slower speed of turning.

The baseboard can be built up from 9-in. planking and requires no special comment beyond saying that it should be as large and substantial as convenient. Within limits, the three main units may be placed to suit the type of board available.

## THE VARIABLES

Now consider the several variables at your disposal.

(*a*) The circle size may be altered by shift of the pen (at the center of its stroke) relative to the center of rotation of the table. This determines the general size of the pattern.

(*b*) The stroke or amplitude of pen travel may be varied by selection of the required eccentric hole. This controls the depth of loops or scalloping.

(*c*) The ratio of reciprocating pen frequency to rotation frequency may be varied widely by choice of gear wheels, then finely adjusted by the cone gear. This fixes the number of waves or petals per turn.

(*d*) The limit of the pen throw may not reach, or

may just reach, or may pass right across the center of the design, producing waves, scallops, petals, or double loops.

(*e*) The pen movement may be skew or directed eccentrically from the center of the turntable.

(*f*) Repetition of the exact same path will occur only if the ratio of frequencies is maintained precisely; a slight discrepancy from the whole number will result in a shifting phase and an interlacing network of lines.

In general, the pen and paper motions are being united into one trace. The variations resulting are wide but not unlimited; they are readily classified. In every case the mechanism compounds a circular platform motion with a straight-line reciprocating pen motion. If the pen were at rest — that is, if the crank pin were actually in the center hole of the crank bar — then a perfect circle should result, its radius being the pen displacement from the center of the turntable. What is a circle? Those familiar with Lissajous' figures will realize that a circular motion itself results from compounding similar Simple Harmonic Motions (S.H.M.) at right angles, the phase displacement being 90°. This compounding is already inherent in the circular motion of the paper, and we propose to superimpose a further S.H.M. Conceivably then, if the frequencies and amplitudes were identical, the pen movement might just annul one of the component

S.H.M.'s of the circle and leave us with a straight-line trace again. This reduction to linear movement by cancellation of one S.H.M. would require such careful adjustment as to be improbable in practice; an ellipse would be more likely, and with slight phase error this would slowly rotate.

If this model is compared with the case of the pendulum harmonograph, the time periods of platform and pen here simply depend on the rate at which we rotate the handle, and of course if this is not a uniform rate the reciprocating movements cannot be called "Simple Harmonic." This is not important, however, as it will not affect the compounded shape: the ratio of the time periods and movements are the same whatever the rate at which the handle is turned. One notable difference from pendulum-drawn harmonograms becomes evident as the trace undergoes repeats. Unless the ratio cone has been very carefully adjusted in height so as to give a constant figure, a slight displacement occurs at each cycle and a fine mesh of lines results. This may be reminiscent of the effect of amplitude diminution in harmonograms, but of course no such decrease occurs in schemagrams; the displacements are simply rotational ones.

These sidewise displacements often give rise to a twisted, ribbonlike appearance, as in Fig. 8D and L. When drawn with a fine pen and very closely overlaid at fine angles the moiré or watered-silk effects common in harmonograms may be observed, but for clarity of reproduction the illustrations here show only coarse line figures. A further point of contrast should be noted. Since the paper has no particular phase, the *relative* phase of pen and paper becomes meaningless and the usual Lissajous phase difference does not arise. On the other hand, phase *shift* between one cycle and the next does result in complex pattern forming. If there is no phase shift, then the pen just retraces the same path at every revolution of the turntable and continued turning just blackens the basic line, as in schemagrams $A$, $C$, $F$, and $H$ (Fig. 8).

METHOD OF USE

The technique of using the model is fairly obvious, but some such procedure as follows might well be adopted.

(*a*) Set the cone about halfway down the cone springs and choose a lower pulley which gives roughly the required ratio of pen transits to each table rotation.

(*b*) Rotate the table once and count the number of turns the eccentric makes, by using marked spots on each. If the pen reciprocation is too fast or too slow to give the integral ratio number wanted, the cone must be adjusted to correct this.

Remember that raising the cone speeds up

the pen (more scallops per turn) and lowering
slows the pen relative to the turntable (fewer
scallops per revolution).

(*c*) Decide on the pen-lever projection—the position of the pen relative to the center of the circles when the pen is in the middle of its sweep.
This partly controls the size of the design.

(*d*) Determine the size of the indentations or loops
by setting the crankpin in the appropriate hole
in the volute.

(*e*) Make a rough test with a ball-point pen and
cheap duplicating paper to check the pattern
and the phase displacement of successive turns.

(*f*) Using smooth paper and a fine pen correctly
adjusted for height, attempt the actual design.

(*g*) Make a note on the design of the various set-
tings of the schemagraph if there is any possibility of wishing to reproduce it again.

## NOTES ON THE SCHEMAGRAMS IN FIG. 8

Some of the main forms assumed by schemagrams are
illustrated in the accompanying diagrams, which have
been selected to show basic types rather than for their
delicacy or artistic effect.

(A) This shows a frequency ratio of 4:1—that is,
four scallops of small indentation.

(B) 3:1. A more indented trefoil with a fairly rapid
phase shift.

(C) 4:1 again, but with even smaller indentation than (A), and now a number of cycles have been completed with shifting phase.

(D) The tooth effect is more conspicuous in this 7:1 and in the higher ratios.

(E) In this 9:1 ratio the skew throw produces a ratchet-tooth appearance.

(F) 4:1. The throw here reaches the center and results in petal forms. In this quatrefoil the linear motion is not quite centered.

(G) Again 4:1, with only two cycles drawn for clarity, but now the throw crosses the center and forms double loops.

(H) 5:1. Here the pen reciprocation is no longer directed at the center of the circle. The phase shift has been small enough for the lines to solidify.

(I) The twisted-ribbon appearance is commonly produced.

(J) 4:1. The pen reciprocation is not directed toward the center.

It will be appreciated by mathematically minded readers that all these symmetrical primary curves are capable of exact expression in algebraic form, in the same manner as ellipses, hypocycloids, epicycloids, and the like. The many variables would make expressions for these curves very complex, however, even using polar coordinates.

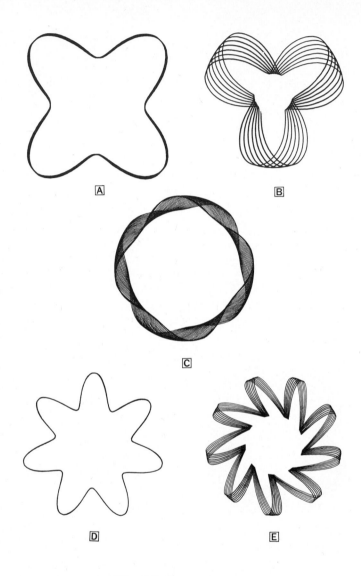

*Fig. 8 Schemagrams*

*Fig. 8 Schemagrams*

# 4   A WATER MOTOR
## AND AN ALTERNATOR

### THE WATER MOTOR

The water wheel, fitted with vanes or paddles, was one of the earliest of primitive sources of power for driving mills and other machinery and is still used where oil and coal for steam generation are not conveniently available.

Most people are familiar with the mill-wheel principle and may know that overshot and breastshot wheels are more efficient than the undershot type (see Fig. 9). The modern form of the mill wheel is the turbine, and the world's hydroelectric plants use massive turbogenerators for conversion of the energy of falling water into electric power.

*32*

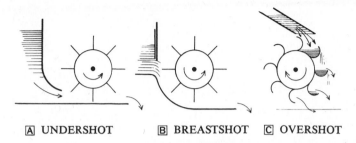

A UNDERSHOT     B BREASTSHOT    C OVERSHOT

*Fig. 9 Water wheels*

One may broadly distinguish between two types of turbine. Those which use huge quantities of water at low pressure employ the Francis, or reaction, form of rotor. The water is ejected from the rotor itself, which revolves in the reverse direction. In this respect it is like the old Hero steam engine.

Those turbines utilizing high-pressure water employ the Pelton or De Laval type rotor. Here, the vanes respond, again by reaction, to impulse from high-velocity jets. A system of revolving vanes continuously redirects the stream until its energy is absorbed. Sir Charles Parsons pioneered the design of impulse-reaction turbines using expanding steam and brought them to an unprecedented state of efficiency. In modern turbogenerators the maximum power is extracted from the input by employing the ideal configuration and number of blades in rotors which allow for successive stages of steam expansion. Very high speeds of rotation are attained, and these, while suited to some purposes, often have to be geared down for generation of electricity and for ship propulsion.

The present water-driven model bears little relevance to the beauty and efficiency of the modern turbine, but insofar as impulse and reaction are involved it does clearly illustrate conversion of mechanical or hydraulic work into electrical energy. Despite the low efficiency of this conversion the construction of the model is fun and not too difficult even with simple tools.

To make the water turbine, first obtain some close-grained wood about 1 in. thick and cut a 9-in. square from it (*A* in Fig. 10). Using a coping saw, cut out the 6-in.-diameter circular hole and the channel marked *H*. The long tongue at the bottom is less likely to break off accidentally if the grain of the wood runs parallel to the lower edge. As the plate should be flat, the wood ought to show no sign of warping. The inside cut edge of this frame should be smoothed off with a half-round file. Two square plates are to be bolted to the frame already cut; they may be of Masonite or even plywood, but, if available, $\frac{3}{16}$-in. or $\frac{1}{4}$-in. Lucite sheet is preferable, since the rotor is then visible.

For the water nozzle *F*, roll up a conical tube of sheet tin or brass. Solder the seam and solder a ring of copper binding wire around the top edge as shown. The jet should taper from the wide end, about the diameter of garden hose pipe, to about ⅛ in. at the tip. Drill the oblique hole for this in the center frame in two stages, using bits of different diameter; push the nozzle tightly into the wood and glue it in position with epoxy cement.

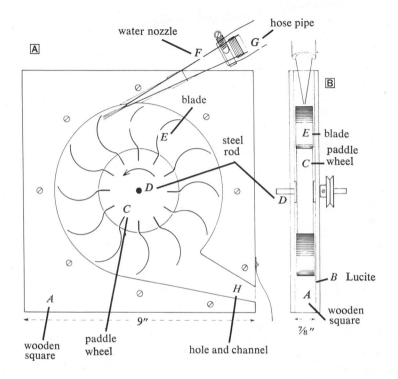

*Fig. 10 The water turbine*

The side plates are to be bolted on with 1½-in. nuts and bolts, but before this is done the wood should be immersed in melted candle wax in a tin tray. Soaked thus in paraffin wax, the wood will be impervious to water and less likely to warp in use.

Next construct the paddle wheel on a central wooden disk of 2½-in. diameter, which should be cut from hardwood, slightly thinner than the main frame. Accurately mark out the twelve radial slots 30° apart and, with a hacksaw, cut each to a depth of ⅜ in. Make the blades from aluminum or brass sheet, cutting and bending them all to the same spoon pattern *E*. They should be friction-tight in the slots, but glue them also with epoxy cement.

Drive a ¼-in. steel rod *D* through an exactly central hole in the rotor; if this shaft is a good tight fit it should require no gluing. As with the other woodwork, saturate the rotor with molten paraffin wax. Make sure it is weight-balanced on the shaft, clipping the blades if necessary. Also make sure that the blades clear the nozzle and sides of the casing when the spindle is mounted in the bearing holes drilled in the Lucite side plates. These holes must be a good fit on the shaft and truly in line. Alignment may have to be improved by enlarging the bolt holes on one of the side plates, making it capable of some adjustment, but in any case the rotor must spin freely. Large washers on each side of the center disk will prevent the escape of water from the bearings. The bearings should be well lubricated.

Attach the hose pipe *G* from the cold-water supply to the jet *F* with an ordinary screw hose-clamp. The tapered nozzle brings the water jet to a high velocity for impact with the blades, and this determines their angular velocity. No figures can be given for speed of rotation or the power available, as this is entirely dependent on the pressure of your water supply, but if this tap-water pressure is too low the results will certainly not justify the work of making the turbine. Pulleys of various diameter may be mounted on the shaft, and the water motor may be suitably geared up or down to drive other models. The turbine must be used over a sink, and the addition of a wide pipe or a shield of bent metal may be necessary to channel the outflow of water.

You may well find that the performance of the motor can be improved by alteration of the shape of the blades or the size of the nozzle. Examine the behavior of the rotor at various speeds by adjusting the flow from the tap. If water is being carried up the right-hand side by the blades their rotation will clearly be impeded. Also, pressure reduction below the blades on the right would reduce the speed, and so the clearance must be such as to allow air to enter.

## THE ALTERNATOR

This electrical device constructed for use with the water motor is a simple form of a.c. generator.

When the magnetic field through a coil alters in intensity, perhaps by completely reversing its direction, an induced electromagnetic force (e.m.f.) is set up in the wire. This, in a completed circuit, engenders a fluctuating or alternating current; notice that the electrical pressure exists only while the field is actually changing. We are dependent on this simple fact of electromagnetic induction for our supply of electrical power.

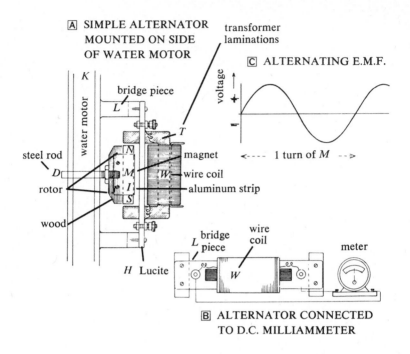

A SIMPLE ALTERNATOR MOUNTED ON SIDE OF WATER MOTOR

transformer laminations

C ALTERNATING E.M.F.

voltage

K

bridge piece

water motor

L

T

steel rod

D

rotor

wood

N

M

I

S

magnet

wire coil

aluminum strip

←---- 1 turn of *M* --→

H Lucite

L bridge piece

wire coil

W

meter

B ALTERNATOR CONNECTED TO D.C. MILLIAMMETER

*Fig. 11 The alternator*

Whether the magnet *M* (Fig. 11A) moves relative to the wire *W* or vice versa, the flow through the coil changes and current is created. When the magnet *M* revolves at a steady speed, the e.m.f. (and current) in coil *W* is said to be alternating in sinusoidal fashion (Fig. 11C) and the device would be called a simple alternator.

Perhaps you have investigated the generator of a bicycle lamp; almost certainly it is a device of this type. Fig. 12 shows the armature to consist of a small but

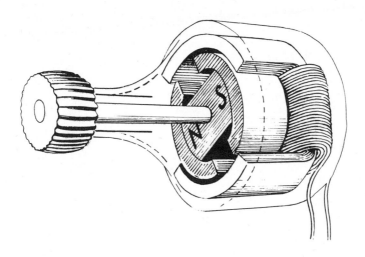

*Fig. 12 The bicycle generator construction*

powerful permanent magnet made of a retentive alloy. It is built up with pole pieces into cylindrical form and magnetized with north and south poles set diametrically. When the small friction wheel on the end of the shaft engages with the bicycle wheel, the magnet is revolved at high speed. The curved, soft-iron pole pieces between which the rotor spins are extensions of the core on which the coil is wrapped, and the alternating current is induced in this coil. Large industrial alternators work on this principle, except that the rotor is an electro-magnet and not a permanent one. The efficiency and power of this simple arrangement depend on the minute gap between the armature and fixed pole pieces, an accuracy achieved by the use of machine tools. For this reason good generators are generally more difficult to construct than motors, and for most amateur model makers the task is likely to yield disappointing results.

Naturally, the requisite input of mechanical work is increased as the gap between the stationary and revolving poles is made smaller, but the stray field is reduced. Run in reverse, motors do not usually make good generators, although a d.c. generator can often be used as a motor. Obviously the a.c. bicycle generator could not be run as a motor by injection of current.

To start the present model, a pile of old transformer laminations may be cut, by halving, to the shape shown at $T$ in Fig. 11A. They are bound solid with cellophane tape and then neatly wrapped with half a dozen layers of copper wire of about gauge 23. An Alnico or Alcomax magnet which will just revolve in the gap between the arms forms the rotor $NS$, and the coil wound on the nonlaminations forms the stator $W$. Magnets of retentive alloys are now made in a great variety of shapes and sizes, and if one of cylindrical form, magnetized diametrically, is obtainable it will be preferable to the bar magnet illustrated, since the aforementioned pole gap will be uniform and smaller.

The magnet is shown clamped by an aluminum strip to a block of wood which is drilled to screw tightly onto the tapped end of the water-turbine shaft. One advantage of spinning the magnet rather than the coil lies in the fixed connection of the wires. On the other hand, any undue vibration tends to demagnetize the rotor.

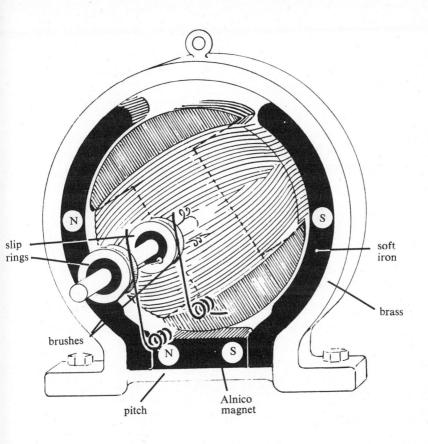

slip rings

soft iron

brass

brushes

pitch

N    S
Alnico magnet

*Fig. 13 A toy a.c. generator*
*(bearings, terminals, and end cover removed)*

In the usual arrangement of a.c. generators the coils spin on their armature inside the magnetic field. This involves tapping off the current by way of two brushes which press against slip rings joined to the ends of the armature winding. The rings are mounted on, and revolve with, the shaft. A manufactured toy generator of this type, employing a permanent magnetic field, is shown diagrammatically in Fig. 13. It will be seen that a powerful field magnet is mounted in the base and its pole pieces are held in position by attachment to the outer casting. The slip rings are simply brass pulleys insulated from the shaft, and wire springs resting in their grooves constitute the brushes. A very small generator of this pattern, driven at high enough speed by pulley gearing from the turbine, will give the small voltage needed to light a lantern bulb, but unless the water pressure is high the alternator described (Fig. 11) may prove disappointing in this respect. Even so, it well illustrates the a.c. principle involved, and the following experiment should be made.

Join the terminals of the alternator you have made to a center-reading d.c. milliammeter, Fig. 11B, and allow enough water flow to give slow revolution of the turbine. The needle of the meter is seen to swing rhythmically from side to side with increasing amplitude at first, but as the speed of the turbine builds up, the needle assembly in the meter becomes unable to follow the rapid current swing. It just quivers about its zero reading. Now substitute an a.c. meter across the terminals and repeat the experiment. This instrument shows a steady reading (root mean square value) which visibly increases with the speed of the water motor.

With the alternator connected to a 3-volt flashlight

bulb it may be seen that slow rotation does not produce a large enough induced electromagnetic force to light it. Greater speed causes a flickering light, and with further increase the light becomes steady because the filament has not had time to cool between the current surges. With still more speed the fascination of more dazzling light usually leads to a bulb casualty!

By root mean square (r.m.s.) current, we mean that direct current which produces a heating effect equivalent to that of the alternating output from the generator. If the model helps to clarify this topic alone, the time spent in its construction will not have been wasted.

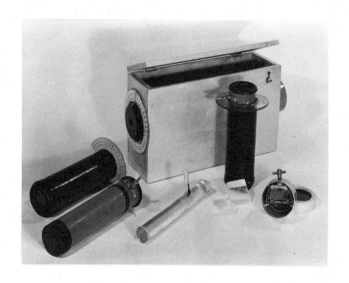

# 5 POLARIZED LIGHT
## AND A POLARISCOPE

There are some vital differences in the natures of
sound and light waves. First, sound requires a material medium such as air to travel through, but light
can travel through a vacuum. Secondly, their speeds
are very different. Both are propagated as waves, the
sound waves in air or other substance, the light as
electromagnetic waves. Both are, in a sense, vibrations, but there is also a third essential difference. In
sound, the vibrations of the particles are *in* the direction in which the wave is traveling (Fig. 14A),
whereas in light the vibrations are *across* the direction
of travel—that is, at right angles to the path (Fig.

*44*

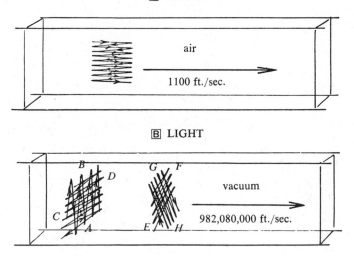

*Fig. 14 Longitudinal and transverse waves*

14B). The sound waves are pressure changes resulting from movements of the air particles, but the light waves may be in a vacuum or some transparent medium. The latter case is more difficult to envisage because the fluctuations are not mere pressure changes but fluctuations of magnetic and electric field. However, the essential point here is that they are crosswise—that is, in all such directions as *AB*, *CD*, *EF*, *GH*, etc. (Fig. 14B). This may be clearer if we think in terms of the following mechanical analogy.

Imagine strings along the box (Fig. 15) being wobbled in all directions in the box, the disturbance being transmitted along the strings as waves. These are

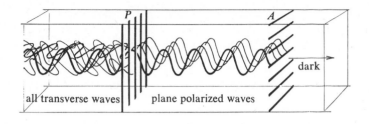

*Fig. 15 Polarization of ordinary light*

transverse waves. Then picture a comb or grid of vertical wires, *P*, in the box through which all the strings pass. Only vertical waves will be able to pass through the comb; all other types will be cut off. A beam of this special sort of vibration is, in the case of light, known as *plane-polarized* light, since something similar to this has happened, limiting the vibrations to one plane (in this case the vertical one). Now consider the introduction of a second comb, *A*, with its slots and teeth horizontal. This will cut off the remaining vibrations and will produce a state of darkness. If the slots in *A* were parallel to those in *P*, the polarized waves would get through both; but total cancellation—that is, darkness—will result from the combs being at right angles to each other. The fact that this sort of phenomenon is possible with a light beam is one of our reasons for stating that it consists of "transverse" waves. Comparable behavior is impossible in the case of sound waves, since in these the vibrations of the particles are in the direction in which the wave is traveling.

Various devices will effect polarization of a beam of light. Tourmaline crystals and specially cut calcite crystals are notably effective in doing it, but even simple reflection from a glass surface will cause polarization to some degree. Thus most reflected light—for example, moonlight, or sunlight reflected from clouds, lakes, or the polished hoods of cars—is partially polarized. Apart from a slight reduction in intensity, our eyes do not notice any special difference between this polarized light and ordinary light.

The polarizing effect of a crystal is related to the particular setting of its axes; thus if a number of individual crystals are used, they must all be set the same way. With this provision they may, in fact, be extremely small.

The material called Polaroid is designed for the purpose of polarizing light, and you may have met it in the form of sunglasses or of special glasses made for viewing stereoscopic movies. It is made as a thin film sandwich in which minute and aligned dichroic crystals (iodosulfate of quinine) are embedded. Although Polaroid polarizes light passing through it, there is little reduction in intensity or color effect noticeable if a single sheet is used. When a light is viewed through two sheets of Polaroid, the light transmitted is seen to increase and diminish in intensity as one piece is rotated relative to the other. From the maximum brightness position a rotation of 90° gives maximum darkness, another 90° gives brightness again, and so on. The darkness is never quite complete; usually a dark purplish tinge gets through the crossed Polaroids. The sheet nearest the light is called the polarizer and the one nearest the eye is referred to as the analyzer. Substances like certain sugar solutions, when placed between the polarizer and the analyzer, can rotate the plane of polarization and thereby alter the setting of the analyzer needed to produce darkness. The rotation involved depends, in size and direction, on the concentration and nature of the solution. This is the basis of instruments called polarimeters and those special ones used for sugar examination known as saccharimeters.

This brings us to the construction of our polariscope model. for which some Polaroid sheet is required. If you can find a discarded pair of Polaroid sunglasses, you can use them. You should be able to buy two 1-in. squares of Polaroid film from a scientific supplier for less than $1.00.

Mount one piece of Polaroid, *A* in Fig. 16, in the end of a tube of plumbers' plastic water pipe *B*, 3 in. long. This material is very useful, since it is strong, easily sawed and drilled, clean, and pleasant to handle. You may be able to get scraps from a plumber. The piping used should be of about 2 in. external diameter and about 1½ in. internally—that is, ¼ in. thick. *B* is rotated by the knob *C*, which is riveted on. The other

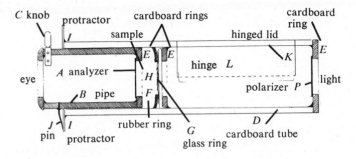

*Fig. 16 Cross section of the polariscope*

piece of Polaroid, *P*, is mounted at the end of a slightly wider tube, *D*, in which the plastic pipe rotates smoothly, but friction-tight. If you have trouble finding a tube of the correct size, it is a simple matter to roll up and glue a cylinder of just the size required. An alternative would be to select two tin cans of suitable diameter with felt or cloth glued around the inner one to equalize the sizes and give smooth rotation. Parts marked *E* in Fig. 16 are rings of thick cardboard with square holes chiseled out slightly smaller than the Polaroid film. They are glued to the tubes and the Polaroid squares are attached to the rings.

The thin glass disk *G* is similarly attached, and a rubber ring, *F*, gripping the tube *D*, can hold against the glass a transparent sample, *H*.

For more advanced experiments involving angle measurement, a 360° celluloid protractor, *I*, has had the center removed with a fret saw so that it can be mounted on the end of the tube *D*. A large pin, *J*, inserted in the plastic pipe acts as a pointer and enables a reading to be made on the scale, indicating the setting of the analyzer Polaroid $A$.

If white light is used and layers of very thin materials such as celluloid, cellophane, or mica are placed between the polaroid sheets (at $H$), very beautiful and brilliant color effects result. Some materials, such as Lucite and glass, need to be in a state of strain to produce this coloration. Certain wave lengths (colors) are blocked out in turn by the arrangement, dependent on the sample's thickness. If the full spectrum has been deprived of one color, its residue, now a brilliant color complementary to the one eliminated, is observed. Rotation of the polaroid analyzer causes these areas of color to pass through a succession of brilliant hues the beauty of which is only realized by personal observation.

For further experiments the instrument is best clamped rigidly to a baseboard. A semicylindrical section $K$ of the tube $D$ is removed with a fine coping saw and then hinged on again with a strip of adhesive tape $L$ before the whole instrument is painted. This enables one to insert glass troughs of optically active liquid between the Polaroids when wishing to use the model as a real polarimeter. For the simplest viewing experiments it would suffice to mount the Polaroids over holes cut in the base and lid of a round tobacco can.

Place a frosted bulb beyond $P$, the polarizer, and

turn the analyzer *A* until the greatest degree of darkness is observed. The Polaroids are then said to be crossed. Greatest light is passed when *A* has been rotated a further 90°; darkness again at 180°; and so on.

For the next experiment prepare a sample as follows: Fold a 2½ -in. square of cellophane or transparent wrapping into an irregular piece of varying thickness (Fig. 17A). Insert this in the tube, Fig. 16, against the glass plate *G* and view the colors. These will alter in a remarkable way as the analyzer *A* is rotated. For example, change in the areas marked (*a*) and (*b*) in Fig. 17A, are seen to be:

  (*a*) Chrome yellow, green, intense royal blue, pale turquoise, cream, lemon.
  (*b*) Gray, magenta, vivid purple, blue, pale green, white.

Many common transparent materials may be investigated in the polariscope, some only showing color effects when in a state of strain. It is interesting to study the optical activity of slips of mica and other crystals similarly inserted as "samples."

Distorted Lucite bars and plates in a state of strain are particularly effective in displaying beautiful color effects: lines of one color indicate regions of one strain value, but the colors change as the stressing screws are turned. Fig. 17B shows a method of straining a piece of Lucite with a nut, bolt, and thick steel-wire loop.

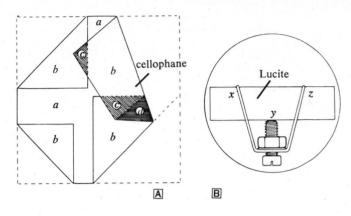

*Fig. 17 Polariscope samples*

The Lucite, of length to fit into the polariscope and about ½ in. broad by ⅕ in. thick, shows a color pattern developing from the stress points $x$, $y$, and $z$ as the bolt is tightened. Strains in large girders and other engineering units can be studied by making models in Lucite and viewing the colors transmitted in specially constructed polariscopes. Obviously this field of study is very wide and further reading is essential for more advanced experiments, but interested readers may care to pursue the subject of polarimetry by devising their own models.

## A LUCITE STRAIN MODEL

From a piece of 2-in.-diameter iron pipe saw off a 1-in. length to make a strong iron ring. Drill a hole in one side and tap a thread in the sole so that a ¼-in. clamp screw can be fitted as shown in Fig. 18. Cut out a

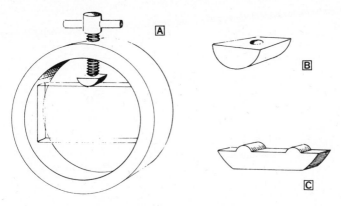

*Fig. 18 Lucite strain device*

rectangular piece of ¼-in. Lucite about ¾ in. wide
and of such length as to fit inside the iron tube.

Tightening up the screw may cause sideways slip of
the Lucite sample, and so it is advisable to fit a little
metal block (*b*) at the screw tip. This not only distributes the stress across the width of the Lucite but also
avoids rotation of the sample with the screw. Stress
points other than those at the bottom corners are
generated by fitting below the Lucite a metal block
filed to the shape shown at (*c*).

As an alternative to using this strain model with the
polariscope already described, it may be made into a
separate instrument. Find a round tin can which just
fits over the iron ring and cut holes in its lid and base
to accommodate the two Polaroids. With the strain
screw projecting from the side of the can a very
compact and satisfactory model may be built up in
this way.

# 6   ELECTROSTATICS

One naturally tends to think of electricity in terms of the flowing current which produces our light and heat—that is, continuous current from batteries, generators, and alternators. This flow of charge was the . concern of Alessandro Volta in 1800, but much earlier, at the end of the sixteenth century, Dr. William Gilbert was studying static electricity—that is, charges normally at rest on insulators and conductors. Today, electrostatics is the natural foundation on which to build the vast superstructure of electronics and particle physics.

Most of the material for the basic experiments that

follow is easily available, and modern plastics greatly simplify experiments formerly made difficult by accidental charge leakage. Glass as an insulator or as a holder of positive charge was a notorious source of annoyance because of its liability to occlude moisture on its surface. This necessitated warming and scrupulous drying for experiments to work well. A Lucite rod rubbed with silk will hold its positive charge for a very long period, and as the surface of polyethylene is not easily wetted it makes an ideal insulator for holding negative static charge. In general, then, we may substitute Lucite for glass and polyethylene for the ebonite suggested for experiments in the older textbooks.

The experiments here illustrate some important electrostatic principles.

(A) THE LAW OF ATTRACTION AND REPULSION

Early experimenters realized that friction of some materials with insulators gave rise to two opposing types of charge, now called positive and negative. They referred to the former as vitreous charge, the type generated on glassy substances rubbed with silk, while the latter, resinous charge, was the negative type engendered when amber or sealing wax was rubbed with flannel. In this sense, Lucite would be regarded as a vitreous material and polyethylene as a resinous one. We now think of these charges as accumulations of displaced electrons, an excess being a negative charge and a deficiency representing a positive charge. Friction between suitable materials causes this displacement of electrons, and, as one might expect, the resulting charges are equal in quantity and opposite in sign.

Given the chance, the charges will right the disturbance; that is, the electrons will flow back again, once more establishing a neutral state. On insulators this may be a very slow process, but between conductors the flow may be almost instantaneous. The sudden transfer of electrons is certainly a current, but it is as much like a battery current as falling over a cliff is like bicycling down a hillside road as a method of reaching the lower level.

Hang up a piece of Lucite, such as a clotheshanger, on a rayon or silk thread and charge it by flicking it with a silk handkerchief. Bring up a similarly charged piece of Lucite and repulsion ensues.

Repeat the experiment using polyethylene objects rubbed with fur or other cloth. This experiment is easily done with a couple of soft plastic pitchers or cups hung up by their handles and charged merely by rubbing with the dry hand. Here again we find repulsion (Fig. 19).

Next do a similar experiment, this time combining a suspended charged Lucite object with an oppositely charged piece of polyethylene. As the unlike charges are seen to pull together we come to the general conclusion:

Unlike charges attract.

Like charges repel.

(B) INDUCTION OF OPPOSITE CHARGE

Cut a foot or so of polyethylene in a strip ½ in. wide, using, for example, plastic shower-curtain material. Charge it by wiping it with a dry cloth or even by running it through the fingers once or twice. Hold it near a wall. It is attracted and sticks to the wall. The reason is that a dissimilar charge, positive, has been induced on the neighboring part of the wall and the positive and negative attract. This is best pictured as electric lines of force linking the surfaces; and since the electric lines of force, which run across from positive to induced and equal negative charges, tend to contract, the objects move together if they can. Thin rubber sheeting behaves in the same way as polyethylene, and a toy balloon which has been rubbed will attach itself to a wall.

By friction, charge a polyethylene cup or rod and hold it near a slow stream of water running from a faucet. The stream is plainly pulled toward the insulator and may curl around it to an astonishing degree (Fig. 20). The attraction results from an opposite charge being induced in the stream of water. The equivalent like charge, displaced to the water tap, is lost to earth.

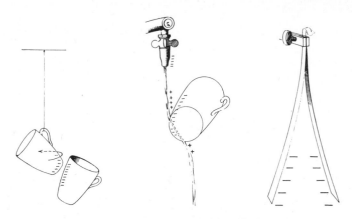

*Fig. 19 Repulsion of a like charge*

*Fig. 20 Attraction of an induced opposite charge*

*Fig. 21 Charged polyethylene strips*

Two strips of polyethylene sheeting, similarly charged and suspended from the same point (Fig. 21), will stand apart for a long period. They eventually collapse together when the charge has leaked away, how soon this occurs being determined by the amount of moisture in the air at the time.

## MAKING AN ELECTROPHORUS

The electrophorus is a very simple device for obtaining a succession of equal electrostatic charges on a metal plate from one original charge on a slab of insulator.

Obtain two shallow tin trays, the larger of which may be a square baking pan (a jelly-roll pan would do) and the other a smaller round cake pan about 1½ in. deep. These pans are usually made with a neat rolled edge—essential for electrostatic charge holding.

Clean off the print from the surface of an empty polyethylene bottle—a discarded small bottle of detergent or bleach would do—by rubbing it with scouring powder on a damp cloth. Flatten the top of the screw cap of the bottle and glue it to the center of the round pan (see Fig. 22). With the inverted bottle screwed in we then have an excellent insulating handle when held well away from the metal plate. Being removable, it is also more easily stored.

Next, a sheet of good insulator to attach inside the larger metal tray is needed. The bottom of an old plastic dishpan would be very suitable. Or cut the top and bottom from a cylindrical plastic bottle and slit the cylinder of polyethylene lengthwise. While hot the sheet is easily flattened into a square. Glued in position in the large pan, this becomes an efficient sheet of insulator, the sole of the electrophorus (Fig. 22).

First warm all the materials and then charge the insulator sheet by flicking it with dry flannel or rubbing it vigorously with a dry dust cloth or a piece of fur. Place the round pan on the polyethylene. Ground it by touching it with a finger. Lift it up by the top of the handle and bring your knuckle near to the pan; a spark, which under ideal conditions may be nearly an inch long, will jump across. This indicates a pressure of thousands of volts.

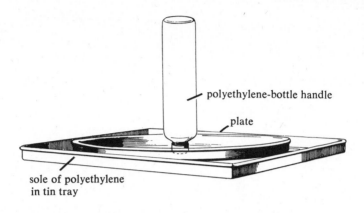

polyethylene-bottle handle

plate

sole of polyethylene
in tin tray

*Fig. 22 The electrophorus*

Although the potential in volts is huge, the actual quantity of electric charge is minute. Evidence to the senses of the energy of the spark lies in the click of sound and the tiny pinprick of shock. It is also quite easy to light a gas jet with the heat of the spark when this is in the correct position relative to the metal edge of the burner.

Where has the energy come from? It derives from the work done in separating the positively charged metal from the negative polyethylene—that is, stretching the electric lines of force (see Fig. 23).

The interesting point about the electrophorus is that once the insulator is charged it does not lose charge with a multitude of repetitions of the plate-lifting operation. At each removal the plate acquires the same quantity of positive charge; this is a useful illustration of inductive charging.

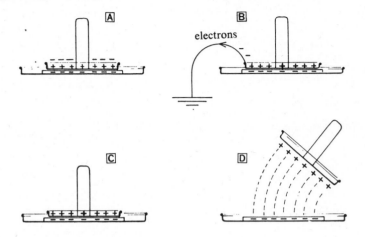

*Fig. 23 Action of the electrophorus*

## DISTRIBUTION OF
## CHARGE ON A CONDUCTOR

Experiments show that charge resides on the surface of a conductor. For this reason a rubber ball painted with aluminum paint or a wooden ball with a coating of tin foil would be equivalent to a solid metal ball, with the advantage of being only a fraction of the weight. Again, if we think of an irregularly shaped conductor the charge is not evenly distributed over the surface but collects more densely on the portions with the biggest curvature. The flatter the area or the bigger the radius of curvature, the less the density of charge. As the capacity for holding charge increases with the radius, one can appreciate the purpose of the vast spherical conductor balls on full-scale Van de

Graaff machines. The opposite extreme is to consider a pointed part of the surface. Here the radius of curvature is very short and the concentration of charge is therefore very high. This shows itself in the tendency for charge to leak away from any points on the conductor, and this fact may be demonstrated by a couple of simple experiments.

(*a*) With Plasticine (the kind of clay sold in toy stores), stick a large pin or sewing needle horizontally onto the knob of a Van de Graaff machine or a Tesla coil. A candle flame brought near to the point (Fig. 24) is seen to be blown away from it as though a draft were streaming from the point, as indeed it is. Air molecules and dust particles in the neighborhood of the point are attracted toward it by the usual process of charge displacement. That is, dissimilar charge to the point is pulled to the side near it, and the particle, charged by induction, is attracted. When near enough, or on actual contact, the particles acquire little charges by sharing and are therefore charged with the same sign (Fig. 25). Repulsion of like charges then flings them violently away from the point, and this we notice as a tiny draught of air. The fuller explanation of the electric wind involves the idea of ionization or splitting of some of the particles into charged portions. This means that atoms or groups have had electrons knocked out of them and the streaming of such particles constitutes the leaking

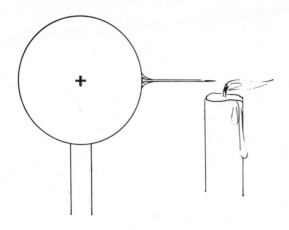

*Fig. 24 Electric wind*

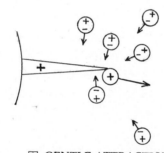

A GENTLE ATTRACTION

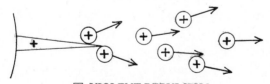

B VIOLENT REPULSION

*Fig. 25 Point action*

charge of the wind. The air, said to be ionized, is thus made conductive, and this is associated with brush-discharge phenomena. In the dark, this type of discharge is noticeable as a purplish light emitted from the point on the conductor.

(*b*) Cut out, with scissors, a thin aluminum can to the shape shown in Fig. 26A or B. Find the balancing point as the center with a ball-point pen and impress an indentation there without actually making a puncture in the aluminum.

Support this little vane on a pin attached to the main conductor of an electrostatic machine. When it is in operation, the little wheel spins around at high speed, driven by reaction from the air streams. Such a device, usually made with more points than two, is known as a Hamilton's Mill. In the dark a bluish ring of light around the wheel indicates the customary brush discharge from points.

## MAKING AN ELECTROSCOPE

An electroscope giving visible indication of a potential difference is, in effect, a high-voltage voltmeter. In its simplest form two charged pith balls hanging together on silk fibers will act in this way. Another instrument which is historically important in the development of electrical science, and which does this more effectively, is the gold-leaf electroscope. Delicate electrometers will measure the effects with great accu-

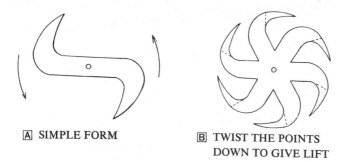

A SIMPLE FORM     B TWIST THE POINTS
                     DOWN TO GIVE LIFT

*Fig. 26 Hamilton's Mill*

racy, but their very sensitivity makes these instruments difficult to operate except under laboratory conditions.

The simple electroscope proved to be one of the most useful instruments in early research. Potential and charge measurement, leakage rate, ionization, and radioactivity were all studied with the aid of the electroscope.

The usual manufactured product employs a strip of gold leaf about ¼ in. wide by 1 in. long attached at the top to a central metal element. This plate and the attached leaf are enclosed in a metal box from which they are electrically isolated by passing through a plug of high insulation—ebonite, sulfur wax, or the like. Windows in the box allow one to see the leaf position. Some forms have two gold leaves; others have only one attached to a polished nickel-plated strip. The leaves are said to "diverge" when a potential difference exists between the central electrode and the metal casing, which is usually grounded.

Gold leaf is extremely thin. Its fragility calls for an especially delicate technique in handling it. When still attached to its backing sheet of tissue and cut with a razor blade it is fairly amenable, but the merest draft of air or the operator's breath will crumple the gold leaf and blow it away. For this reason a more robust though still very sensitive type of leaf has been used in this experiment. The following is an account of a simpler form of instrument. It is easy to construct, since it largely employs kitchen materials.

Obtain a transparent plastic food box, *A* in Fig. 27A. The larger supermarkets and dime stores sell sandwich boxes made of polystyrene or Lucite which are ideal for the casing. Their high insulating quality allows us to dispense with any special plug of insulation for the central electrode *B*. This electrode can be made from a length of ¼-in. brass screw attached at the top to a metal disk. A shallow, round can of the shoe-polish type would be very suitable for the top conductor *C*, but sharp edges, which invite charge leakage, are to be avoided. In the middle of the top end of the plastic box melt a hole of the right size to admit the rod, using a hot wire or a drill. Some plastic is very brittle and liable to fracture if drilled, so if you use a drill you will have to be very careful.

Cut, bend, and polish a brass strip, *D*, about ½ in. wide and 3 in. long and attach it to the lower end of the screwed rod. If this strip can be unscrewed

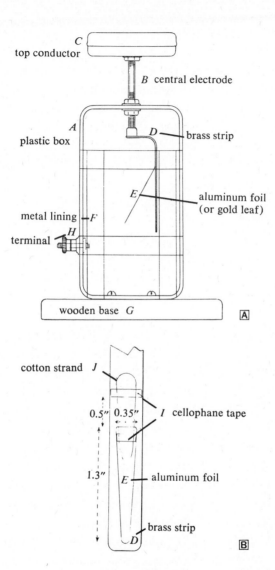

*Fig. 27 The electroscope*

from the rod, replacement of a leaf is simplified. The sides and base of the box are lined with metal, *F*, thin aluminum sheet or metal from a tin can, and the fixing screws through this effectively ground it to the wooden base *G*. A terminal, *H*, is provided for more efficient grounding of the case metal, but for electrostatic purposes the wooden base itself is a conductor and usually forms an adequate ground. Gummed-paper metalized strip is sold for decorative wrapping, and this may be stuck to the box to convert it into a metal casing, but obviously the behavior of the leaf must be visible. Silver cellophane tape is even better, as it adheres well to the plastic. Unless a good proportion of the plastic case is grounded, trouble will be experienced with static charges accidentally produced by handling the case. This results in the leaf apparently going berserk, twisting around and attaching itself to the case in an unpredictable way, but in the grounded casing it is well behaved.

It might be imagined that simple substitution of thin aluminum foil for the gold leaf would make a workable electroscope, but the deflection is very much smaller. The foil may be no more massive than the gold leaf, since gold is over seven times heavier than an equal-sized strip of aluminum; the trouble lies solely in the loss of flexibility at the top hinge. This reduces the sensitivity to an unacceptable degree.

However, this difficulty may be surmounted by the

method indicated in Fig. 27B. Using sharp scissors, cut a tapered strip of ordinary kitchen cooking foil to the shape and dimensions shown—about 1.3 in. long and 0.35 in. at the wide end. Next, separate out one fine strand from a few inches of cotton thread. Wet a loop of this and lay it over the foil placed in position on the brass strip. Cut some cellophane tape ⅛ in. wide and with this attach thread to foil and brass. Do not attempt to substitute silk or rayon for the cotton hinge, as these would be nonconducting. For the same reason do not use cellulose or rubber-based cements for attachment of the cotton. Cotton is extremely flexible, and both it and the adhesive on the cellophane tape have the necessary conductance. Cut off trailing ends of thread and make sure that the back of the foil is clean and free from adhesive so that the slightest tilting of the instrument causes divergence of the leaf. This operation has been described in detail because it forms the heart of the electroscope. Foil is more robust than a gold leaf, but even so this construction requires some patience and neat-fingered work.

Using warm, dry materials, rub a polyethylene rod briskly on a furry or woolen surface and then bring it up to the central conductor disk. The leaf should show a divergence of up to 60° from the plate. Without actual contact no charge has yet been given to the conductor, although charge has been displaced

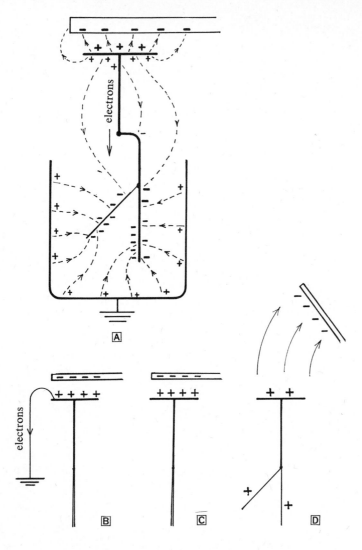

*Fig. 28 Inductive charge displacement
and the stages in positive charging*

in it. As the leaf and its neighbor are then both negative, they repel (Fig. 28A). With removal of the rod the leaf falls.

The following steps result in a positively charged electroscope:

(*a*) Bring the charged rod near the plate (Fig. 28B).

(*b*) Touch the plate with the finger. Bound positive charge remains on top, but the negative on the lower part is neutralized by positive charge drawn from the earth, and the leaf falls (Fig. 28B).

(*c*) Remove the finger from the plate (Fig. 28C).

(*d*) Remove the rod from the proximity of the plate and the positive charge distributes itself over the whole electrode, leaving the leaf deflected (Fig. 28C).

The positively charged instrument can then be used for testing whether a charged body is positive or negative:

If negative, its approach causes the leaf to fall.

If positive, its approach causes an increase in divergence.

The electroscope will normally hold its deflection for an hour or two according to the leakage rate, which is accelerated by any surface humidity. However, the leaf will also collapse through ionization of the air in the instrument, a condition resulting, for example, from proximity of radioactive material, or illumination with ultraviolet light.

## MAKING LEYDEN JARS

A capacitor or condenser consists of two conducting plates separated by a thin layer of insulating material called the dieletric. It could, for instance, be two sheets of metal foil separated by an air gap, waxed paper, or mica. This device has the property of storing electric charge; and when one sheet of foil is raised to a potential or voltage very different from the other one, the insulating layer between them is in a state of electrical strain. This strain is released when the plates are joined. A rapid discharge, oscillatory in nature, occurs when the air gap is sufficiently reduced; it shows as a bright spark in which the air insulation has collapsed.

One type of capacitor of historic importance is the Leyden jar; in fact the unit of capacitance was at one time called the jar. The Dutchman to whom the invention of the device is ascribed apparently survived an almost lethal shock in the course of his investigations. Leyden was the town where Musschenbrok was working when he made the chance discovery in 1746.

The Leyden jar itself has not altered in pattern for over two hundred years, but it is, in fact, easy to construct a modernized and better form using materials available in most kitchens. Radio capacitors are readily and cheaply available in all ranges of capacitance, but our objective is a large breakdown voltage. The particular virtue of the Leyden jar over other forms of condenser lies not in the large capacity, since this is small compared with some tiny modern capacitors (especially the electrolytics), but rather in its very high insulation, which enables it to withstand huge voltage differences.

As a piece of equipment for the model maker the conventional Leyden jar is inconvenient, since the dielectric is a fragile glass cylinder or beaker. To give high capacity the glass must be thin. This, coupled with shocks sustained accidentally, must have caused in schools over the years a staggering mortality of Leyden jars, if not of pupils. We therefore substitute polyethylene for glass. Obtain a cylindrical polyethylene jar (some bleach and detergent comes in such jars), and wash and dry it. Then scrape or dissolve the paintwork from the top half. The inner conducting surface is, in this case, a graphite layer and is prepared as follows:

Mix some powdered graphite or, if you can find it, stove polish with enough liquid glue to make it more viscous. Pour a teaspoonful or so into the bottle without contaminating the neck. Tilt and rotate the bottle until a layer slightly more than half the depth of the inside wall is covered. Using a tube, pipette out any surplus of the syrupy black fluid and leave the open bottle in a warm place to dry. This may take some time, as evaporation is so restricted. At the tacky stage it is advantageous to drop in an ounce or two of glued lead shot. This helps the conductivity and also makes the bottle more stable on its base.

Cover the lower half of the outside of the bottle with aluminum cooking foil. Neatly fasten the edges with a vertical strip of cellophane tape. Press the foil tightly around the bottle and stick further bands of cellophane tape around it, especially at the top edge. The metal crushed over the bottom of the bottle should be left bare. Next, prepare a brass rod with a metal (or metalized) ball on top. Pass the rod through a rubber stopper which fits the neck of the bottle and attach a chain, the kind used on old sink plugs, to the lower end of the rod. This, making contact with the graphite layer, forms the inner electrode and completes our Leyden jar (see Fig. 29).

The thin polyethylene of the bottle not only ensures a large capacitance but avoids the propensity to dampness which glass Leyden jars invariably exhibit.

A capacitor made as above is very suitable for use with the Tesla coil described in Chapter 8. Two such bottles, with their bases joined and grounded, may be attached to the terminals of a Wimshurst or a Van de Graaff machine, and sparks up to 1 in. long may be drawn from them.

Particular emphasis must be laid on the dangerous nature of these jar discharges. The bottle condensers are potentially dangerous if used carelessly, and this warning must be seriously observed. As indicated in

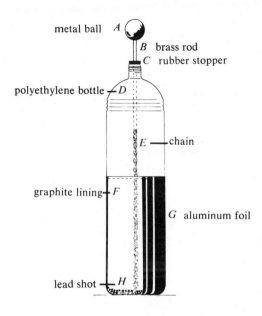

metal ball    *A*

*B*   brass rod

*C*   rubber stopper

polyethylene bottle *D*

*E* —— chain

graphite lining *F*

*G*   aluminum foil

lead shot —— *H*

*Fig. 29 Modernized Leyden jar*

Fig. 30, discharging tongs are easily constructed from a length of springy wire and two small polyethylene bottles which serve as handles. When holding them, keep the fingers well away from the wire in discharging the homemade jars. Link the outer foil and the central electrode to spark off the discharge. After a minute or so, again discharge the jar. The whole strain is not released in the first spark, and an unpleasantly large secondary discharge can occur later.

Another form of capacitor on the same principle can easily be constructed from polyethylene sheet sandwiched between two sheets of aluminum foil. The

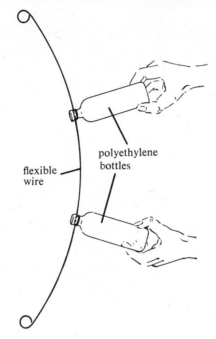

Fig. 30 Discharging tongs

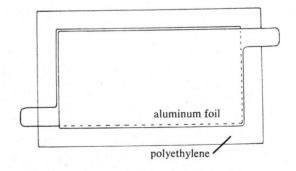

Fig. 31 Foil-sandwich capacitor

metal sheets are cut to the shape shown in Fig. 31, and the dimensions of the polyethylene should allow it to overlap the aluminum by about two inches all around. The whole may then be conveniently wrapped on the outside of the weighted plastic bottle. From the standpoint of dielectric strength, the thicker, tough packaging polyethylene sheet which has a waxlike feel is preferable to the very transparent sheet. The actual capacity in microfarads will be proportional to the area of metal foil rolled around the bottle. Again, and in conclusion, take care not to discharge such a capacitor through your own body.

# 7  A DOUBLE-ACTING
HIGH-VOLTAGE GENERATOR

Research in particle physics, the study of the ultimate building bricks of nature, has necessitated construction of sources of very high voltage. These large electric fields are needed to accelerate bombarding particles such as helium ions (alpha particles) and impart to them the huge energy required for their work of atom smashing. Great varieties of voltage generator, from the voltage multipliers of Cockcroft and Walton to the Bevatrons at Geneva and Brookhaven, have sprung from the joint efforts of physicists and engineers. Because of its apparent simplicity the Van de Graaff type of machine, which produces

*78*

energies in the intermediate range—a few million volts—has attracted much attention. Their discharges, sensibly applied, are harmless because of the low current (amperage), but the impressively long resulting sparks are spectacular by reason of the high pressure (voltage).

The apparatus to be described is of the Van de Graaff type. This model grew, in the first place, out of an attempt to use everyday household materials. Secondly, the vertical height had to be small to facilitate storage. Thirdly, it was to be double-acting, developing charges of opposite sign on the two main conductors.

The self-imposed condition of confining the material to that from household stores, feasible in itself, proved to be an irksome limitation. While the model was somewhat cynically referred to as the "Van de Woolworth" machine, we in fact also drew upon the resources of a hobby shop as a source of Lucite rods and sheets.

The conspicuous large metal spheres of a Van de Graaff are not readily available, and therefore for the prime conductors it was decided to make use of spherical glass light shades of a common size, about 9½ in. in diameter with a smooth-edged 4-in. aperture. The globes were to be surface-treated to render them conducting, as they were to simulate large, hollow spun-metal spheres with highly polished surfaces.

The globes were lightly shellacked, for the sake of

adhesion, and were given a coating of varnish heavily impregnated with the fine aluminum dust used in silver paint. When absolutely dry, this was rubbed down with the finest emery, prior to being given a final coat of smooth aluminum paint. The insides of the globes were similarly metalized with aluminum, but polishing was omitted there.

It is disadvantageous to have edges of the apertures conductive and exposed, because of charge leakage from high curvature; the rims were therefore encased in thick rubber tubing which had been split lengthwise, and the ends joined with rubber cement. Although charge had to be able to flow over the edge from the internal to the external surface, the thick rubber appeared effectively to limit charge leakage there. Electric charge, conveyed by the belt to the inner surface of the globe, is immediately transferred to the outer face and this, being of large radius and area, is capable of rising to a very high potential.

Two large polyethylene bottles with plastic caps were used as rigid insulating supports for the spheres. Good-quality pitch (which you can get from a plumbing-supply house) was melted in an old pan, and care was taken not to ignite it. The empty bottles were clamped down in a bucket of cold water and the molten pitch was then carefully poured in until they were full. In this way very substantial support rods, 2¾ in. in diameter and 10 in. high, were formed. Their

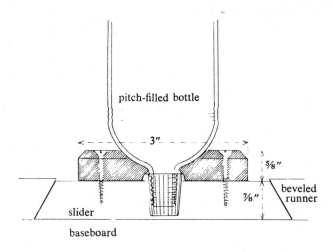

pitch-filled bottle

3″

5/8″

7/8″

beveled
runner

slider

baseboard

**A** ADJUSTABLE METHOD OF MOUNTING MODULATOR

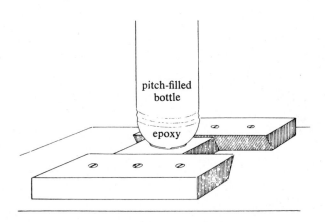

pitch-filled
bottle

epoxy

**B** SLIDE METHOD OF FIXING BASE

*Fig. 32 Generator base mounting*

insulating property was checked by holding one end against the plate of a charged electroscope; the leakage proved to be negligible.

The caps of the bottles, conveniently fluted and made of a hard plastic, were not discarded, but were used as screw-in supports for the inverted bottles. A 3-by-3-in. wooden plate with a central hole was used to clamp each cap to the baseboard, as shown in Fig. 32A and B. This arrangement allowed the cap to be rotated if the need arose later in aligning the apertures of the globes. The distance between centers of the two caps was 30 in., as was the spacing of the outer rollers (*A* and *B* in Fig. 33). Since the bases of the bottles were already conveniently hollowed, they accepted the curvature of the globes, which were attached with epoxy glue. The resin and its acidifier were allowed to set for 3 days; the joint of glass to polyethylene proved to be immensely strong. Each globe, supported as shown in Fig. 33, could be withdrawn endwise from the belt-carrying unit. This made for easy adjustment of pulleys and collector combs.

While it is possible to use materials other than rubber for the charge-carrying belt—for example, silk, polyethylene sheet, or even cloth—on small machines such as this pure rubber has definite advantages of flexibility and durability. It was therefore made from good-quality rubber, actually a strip of first-aid tourniquet rubber 2½ in. wide. This might be obtained

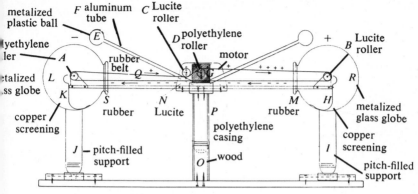

*Fig. 33 Double-acting high-voltage generator*
*(elevation—not to scale)*

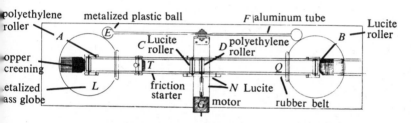

*Fig. 34 Double-acting high-voltage generator*
*(plan—not to scale)*

from a surgical-supply dealer. The ends were neatly
tapered and vulcanized together with rubber cement,
so making a belt of requisite length to stretch around
the various rollers.

Reference to Fig. 33 will show that besides the end
rollers *A* and *B,* 30 in. apart, there were two intermediate ones, *C* and *D. D* was the drive roller, to
the spindle of which a small electric motor was directly attached. Roller *C* served the purpose of in-

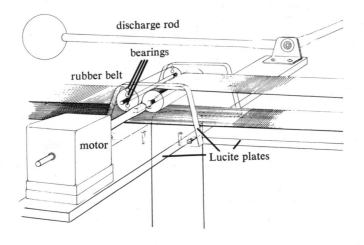

*Fig. 35 The drive-roller assembly*

creasing the area of grip by the belt on the drive roller. It also allowed for variable adjustment of the tension of the belt, since the spindle could be located in other bearings as desired (see Fig. 35).

The rollers were constructed accurately; ¾-in. Lucite rod was cut to 2¾-in. lengths and the ends trimmed in a lathe. While it was still in the step chuck of the lathe the center hole for the shaft was drilled, starting from each end. The Lucite rods were then driven, friction-tight, onto shafts of ⅛-in. steel rod. If solid polyethylene rod for rollers *A* and *D* is not available, an alternative method of making the rollers is to buy from the drugstore small round polyethylene bottles. With their shoulders cleanly cut off, the bottles may be pushed onto wooden rods of suitable size,

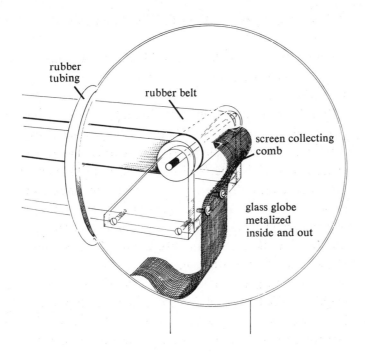

rubber tubing

rubber belt

screen collecting comb

glass globe metalized inside and out

*Fig. 36 Transference of charge*

and these should be accurately mounted on steel spindles, as with *B* and *C*.

The roller *B* in the right-hand collector globe *R* (Fig. 33) is of Lucite, while the other one, *A* in globe *L*, is of polyethylene. Charge removal from the belt is effected by collector combs inside the globes. These are strips of aluminum or copper screening 2 in. wide, set with the top edge of points directed toward, and about ⅛ in. away from, the moving belt. The screening should be screwed to the end of the Lucite bar and it should be long enough to lie inside the globe, making good contact with the aluminum paint there (see Fig. 36).

It will be seen that the belt alternately passes over polyethylene and Lucite rollers and the general effect is the transference of electrons from $R$ to $L$. The exact explanation of the mechanism of this electron pumping might form the basis of an interesting research project, but it seems probable that friction always plays some part in the generation of initial charge, followed by the usual inductive build-up. In our machine a friction starter was included; it took the form of a strip of felt glued in a slotted bar which could be initially turned down to rub on the top of the belt (see Fig. 37). Although its inclusion is not essential, it was found to improve the ease of starting by providing the initial charge on the belt. Large-scale machines do this continuously by a different method. They spray onto the belt, from a row of sharp points, a high-voltage charge supplied by specially designed transformers. The two hinged discharge rods shown in the photograph were made from curtain rods fitted with 3-in. balls. You can use either plastic or sponge-rubber balls, and they should be metallized in the same way that the main spheres were. Other details of the construction can be determined clearly by referring to the diagrams in this chapter.

Flexing and stressing of the rubber in its passage

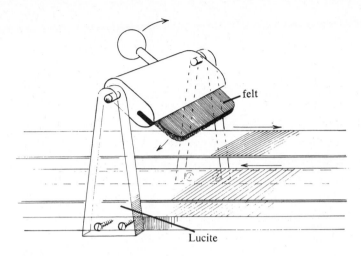

felt

Lucite

*Fig. 37 The friction starter*

from roller $C$ to roller $D$ (Fig. 33) sets up internal strains and energy transfer between layers. This, coupled with forcible separation of the rubber from the polyethylene, effects a transfer of electrons to the latter. The denuded, and hence positively charged, rubber enters the right-hand sphere $R$ and by corona discharge from the screen acquires a stream of electrons supplied by that sphere. The exterior surface of globe $R$ thus builds up a large positive charge. Meanwhile the belt being drawn out of $R$ acquires extra negative charge by induction from the neighboring positive side which it is racing past, and these electrons are withdrawn by the point action of the screen in $L$. Globe $L$ therefore builds up a huge negative charge on its exterior in this "compound interest" manner. The upper limit of potential difference between $L$ and $R$ is set by their capacity, which is dependent on radius, and by the perfection of their insulation, or leakage rate. In any case, the stored electrical energy is derived from mechanical opposition to the belt being driven along and therefore comes from the electric motor, thus constituting a rather curious transformer derivation of high static energy from a low-voltage source.

One suspects that careful analysis might reveal an unexpectedly high efficiency in the conversion of actual mechanical energy into electrical work, one which, by proper design, might constitute a serious rival to conventional dynamos. An antidote to such speculation, however, is that the present machine produces a very trivial amperage: about one microampere results from a belt movement of 50 sq. in. per second!

When you have constructed this model, or, better still, one of your own designing, there are innumerable experiments to be tried.

(*a*)  Make sparks of impressive length from globes to knuckles without any great discomfort.

(*b*)  Make adjustments to obtain, and then measure, the longest spark obtainable between the discharge knobs under ideal dry conditions. Incidentally, longer discharges result from setting the discharging knobs below rather than above the level of the globes. Is this because more electrostatic lines of force from the globes are already heading toward the ground and not to the more distant ceiling?

(*c*) Run the generator in the dark and discover just where the greatest leakages are occurring. These are clearly shown up by corona discharges—usually at pointed surfaces overlooked in the design. Try to eliminate the losses.

(*d*) Bring your hand near either globe and your fingernails will glow brightly.

(*e*) Stand on a rubber mat or a board resting on upturned tumblers, and lean toward a globe. One's hair, if dry, will stand on end in a surprising manner.

(*f*) Hold a pin or nail with its point toward one globe. A purplish glow appears on the point and the sparking, previously in evidence between the globes, at once ceases.

(*g*) Hold the flat surface of a large round cake pan or nut can near enough for bright sparks to pass. At each discharge one notices the slight mechanical kick given to the pan. The force of attraction just before the spark is followed by repulsion.

(*h*) A candle flame is blown away from a pin attached to a globe (see Fig. 24, page 63).

(*i*) Attach some 6-in. cotton threads to one globe and they stand out radially. They are, in fact, indicating the direction of electric lines of force in the immediate vicinity of the sphere.

(*j*) Bring a finger toward some longer threads or strips of tissue paper stuck to the globe. They appear to grasp the finger.

(*k*) Cover a rubber ball with aluminum paint. Draw an astonished-looking face on this and glue onto the ball a mop of woolen strands for hair. Place this head on the globe. When the machine is started up, the hair rises as if in fright.

(*l*) Suspend an aluminum-painted table-tennis ball on a long nylon thread so that it hangs between the discharge spheres. When the motor is started the ball will swing vigorously like a demented pendulum.

(*m*) Use a glass tube of about 1¾-in. to 2-in. diameter and 6 in. long, or cut the base off a milk bottle (hot-wire method) and smooth the cut edge on an emery wheel. Alternatively, a sheet of polystyrene can be rolled into a cylinder held with rubber bands, but the glass appears to work better. Pass thick copper wires through end corks as in Fig. 38 and place an aluminum-painted table-tennis ball in the 3- or 4-in. gap between the wires.

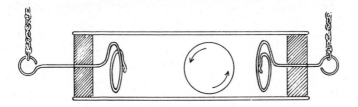

*Fig. 38 Spinning ball experiment*

Attach the discharge globes to the wires, and the ball will spin at such high speed that it often appears to be just a blur. Occasionally it journeys from one electrode to the other and may unexpectedly reverse its direction of rotation. Colored stripes painted on the aluminized ball may be made to show the usual spinning color-top effects. As with Newton's disk, white results from mixing of the pure spectral colors.

(*n*) Suspend a 3- or 4-ft. fluorescent tube (a discarded one will do) alongside the discharge globes. It will light up, though not, of course, as brilliantly as in normal use. Hold one end in the hand and bring the other end near a globe. Radially placed, it will light up, but in a circumferential position it does not fluoresce well. This indicates that the potential fall is radial. Equipotential surfaces are at right angles to the radial directions—that is, spherical.

Electron movement is the basis of our ideas of

electric current as well as of statics, and in the model described we have a versatile machine giving us first-hand contact with phenomena of electron displacement. Information derived from a Van de Graaff used in conjunction with a milliammeter and a clock shows the identity of voltaic and static processes — the latter are simply higher-pressure effects.

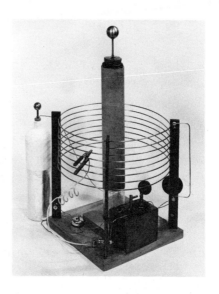

# 8   A TESLA COIL

The danger of electrical models, which can be very real, is not just a matter of voltage; the lethal properties of the discharge depend mainly on the actual current passed through the body. The ensuing shock can affect the nervous system and contract the heart muscles and be fatal even at low electrical pressures if the hands are wet and body conduction good. Experiments with induction coils often do result in high-voltage shock; but as the actual current flow is likely to be minute, the effect is, at most, extremely unpleasant. Another factor, however, must be taken into account—that of frequency.

The frequency of voltage alternation from an induction coil is that of the primary make and break and therefore is usually low. At this frequency the discharge current actually flows through the human body fluids and substance. With a Tesla coil, however, we shall be dealing with very high-frequency alternations, and herein lies the attractiveness of the model. High-frequency (H.F.) currents do not pass through any depth of the body substance but are confined to such a shallow surface layer that muscular contractions are avoided and the pain nerves feel nothing at all. Oddly enough, with frequencies of several megacycles per second the body behaves as a capacitor rather than a conductor. The discharge is, in fact, a surface or skin effect which does not penetrate to the nerves and muscles. For this reason Tesla's apparatus is ideal for the model maker and fascinating experiments can be carried out without danger.

Nikola Tesla, in America, was designing induction motors prior to 1887, which seems somewhat remote from modern physics. The apparatus bearing his name, producing as it did a mere three million volts, might nowadays be regarded as old-fashioned, but historically it is of much interest as an important link with modern practice and as a forerunner of circuits, designed by Cockroft and Walton in England and by Sloan and Lawrence in America, used in early investigations into nuclear structure. Tesla's apparatus is a form of air-spaced step-up transformer with a secondary winding in which big voltages at very high frequency are induced.

A Leyden jar, an induction coil, and the actual Tesla coil are required for this model. The Leyden jar is described on page 72. The induction coil is not difficult to make. Its construction is briefly described below.

The larger the capacity of the Leyden jar and Tesla coil, the larger will be the final output, but a jar of about two-pint size has been found to work well. The dimensions are probably not at all critical, but the model sizes shown here give excellent results.

## AN INDUCTION COIL

Fig. 39 shows the general layout of the induction coil; since the sizes are not at all critical, no dimensions are given. Spool *B*, about 4 in. long in this model, can be made very simply from a tube of cardboard with thick, rigidly fixed end plates. The inner rod *A* is a core of soft iron, laminated insofar as it is made from soft-iron wire. This wire should first be wrapped into a flat coil and then twisted up into a rod, and finally one end should be spread into two wings.

These are screwed onto one end plate of the spool *B*. The core *A* should be trimmed up cylindrically and to some degree solidified by soldering the surface as a matter of convenience, though this partly defeats the

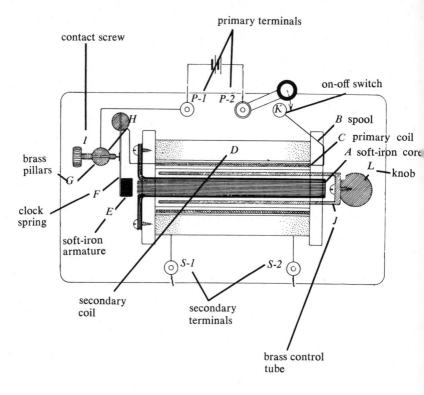

*Fig. 39 Shocking coil*

object of the lamination, reduction of eddy currents. The core should in any case be made smaller than the hole in *B* so that a brass tube, *J*, can form an adjustable sliding sleeve on it.

The first winding on *B* is the primary coil *C*, which is 50 turns of D.C.C. copper wire (A.W.G. 19). Its ends should be brought out to the primary terminals *P-1* and *P-2*. As the primary windings will be inaccessible once the upper layers are wound, its ends have been soldered to twisted double wire with separate insulation on each strand in case of accidental breakage. The primary winding is covered with a layer of waxed paper held in place with cellophane tape. Then the secondary coil *D* is overwound on this level surface. This coil should consist of some 3,000 turns of much thinner wire (A.W.G. 28) and, as each layer is wound, a facing of waxed paper should be overlaid. This keeps the layers flat and neat as well as providing necessary insulation. Again the coil should be finished off with twisted double wire with separate insulation on each strand to avoid damage to the easily cracked single strand of fine wire; this leads to a couple of well-insulated terminals *S-1* and *S-2*.

The make and break of the primary, being essentially similar to that of an electric bell, could probably be made up from available scrap metal. *G* and *H* are two short brass pillars screwed into the baseboard. The pillar *H* rigidly holds one end of a piece of clock spring, *F*, with a small soft-iron armature *E* attached. *G* is a slotted and tapped post which grips the adjustable contact screw *I*. The screw is tipped with nonoxidizable metal and the spring *F* similarly faced with it, since this avoids burned-contact trouble associated with sparking. The rate of buzzing of the vibrator has to be high. This rate is determined by two factors: first, the spring is fairly stiff; and secondly, the soft-iron load must not be too massive. The primary circuit, energized by a 6-volt battery, appears quite isolated from the secondary, but is, of course, linked inductively.

## THE TESLA COIL

The central cylinder of the Tesla coil $C$ (Fig. 40), 16 in. long and 2½ in. in diameter, was in fact a glass cylinder, the base of which was clamped down onto the center of a wooden baseboard, $T$, 1 ft. square and 1 in. thick, by means of a 5-in. square of wood $F$ with a 2½-in. hole in it. Such a cylinder may not be readily available outside of a laboratory, but it is a simple matter to construct a tube of thin cardboard, heavily shellacked and baked, to make a spool for the coil $B$. Some kitchen fluids are at present packed in very tall plastic containers; these, being of high-insulation polyethylene, are ideal for constructing coils of the form required.

The winding $B$ on the cylinder consists of some 400 close turns, in one layer, of A.W.G. 23, D.C.C., or enameled copper wire. This occupies the central part, about 1 ft., of the tube. The top end of the wire is brought out to a metal ball $N$, a 1½-in. brass knob mounted on a rubber plug, $Q$, in the top of the cylinder. The coil $B$ in the center of the apparatus is a secondary winding in which the high-frequency, high-voltage output is induced, and the knob at the

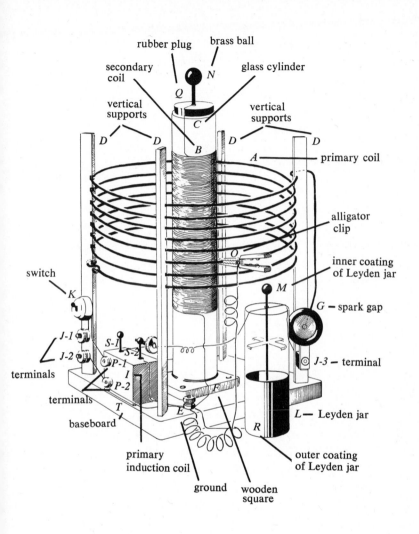

Fig. 40 The Tesla coil

top is the discharging terminal of the apparatus.

As will be seen from the diagrams, the primary coil *A* is extremely well insulated, having only a few widely spaced turns. It can be constructed in the following way:

Cut four lengths of Masonite 12 in. by 1 in. by ¼ in. (*D* in Fig. 40) and mark eight points ¾ in. apart, down one edge of each. At these positions make shallow saw-cuts by using the width of two hacksaw blades clamped in their frame side by side. In any case the width and depth should just accommodate some thick bare copper wire of about A.W.G. 10. If Masonite is unobtainable, strips or rods of Lucite or polyethylene may be substituted, although the latter is somewhat soft. However, rods of a heavy-gauge polyethylene (say, ¾-in. diameter) would serve well, and round holes are easily cut in the baseboard. Drill suitable holes, or saw corner slots, or chisel half through the thickness of the baseboard along the diagonals to take the four rods so that they are rigidly held and glued upright. They form the boundary framework or insulators to carry the heavy copper coil *A*. Thick copper wire is usually obtainable at hardware stores.

On the lower part of two of the upright insulators are mounted the binding posts *J-1*, *J-2*, and *J-3*, the on-off switch *K*, and an adjustable spark gap *G*. Construction of the spark gap is shown separately in

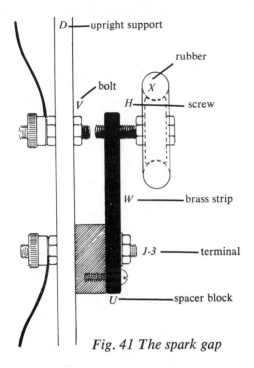

*Fig. 41 The spark gap*

the diagram, Fig. 41. As arrangements here have to be very highly insulated, the knob of the adjuster screw has been enlarged by a thick rubber ring around it, ensuring less chance of leakage to the fingers. Screw *H* works, friction-tight, in a thick brass strip screwed, together with a spacer block, by means of a terminal, *J-3*, to the upright insulator. The upper end of the heavy coil *A* is brought out well away from the other turns of wire and joins the bolt *V*. This and screw *H* form a spark gap adjustable within narrow limits; a gap of between 1 and 2 mm. seems to work well.

The primary induction coil used in the model illustrated happened to be totally enclosed in a rectangular box, *I* (Fig. 40), and this was attached to the baseboard. Its primary terminals *P-1* and *P-2* are linked through the switch *K* (which replaces the switch in Fig. 39) to terminals *J-1* and *J-2* and for operation of the coil these are fed from a 6-volt d.c. supply. The secondary-output spark gap of the induction coil, *S-1* and *S-2*, was set to be much wider than the new gap fitted at *G-H*, and was therefore inoperative.

*S-1* is, as it were, the live terminal of the induction coil *I*. It is attached to the adjuster screw *H* and to the inner coating *M* of the Leyden jar *L*. *S-2* is grounded to terminal *E* on the baseboard, and also grounded at the same point are the lower end of the secondary coil *B*, the outer coating of the Leyden jar *R*, and a tapping *O* on the wide coil *A*. This last movable connection, which is the tuning device, is simply an alligator clip. It is, in fact, grounded, but as a safety measure it has Masonite extensions attached to its sides to make adjustment less hazardous.

Now let us examine the electrical behavior of the apparatus. This induction coil *I* charges, by its high-voltage output, the condenser *L*. But *L* discharges across the small gap *G-H* via some of the coil *A* to the grounded tapping point. Each of the streams of sparks, oscillatory in nature, is essentially a swing of electric charge of enormous frequency. This occurs in the widely spaced coil *A*, which is really the primary of the Tesla transformer. It should be appreciated that the oscillations engendered in *A* are not of the frequency of the make and break of *I*, which, since it is a mechanical vibrator, is not very great. The high frequency depends on the oscillatory character of the spark itself across *G-H*, a radio frequency controlled by the inductance of coil *A* and the capacitance of the Leyden condenser *L*.

The secondary coil *B* picks up these high-frequency oscillations inductively and increases the voltage in the ratio of turns between *B* and *A*. But in order to do this, the important point is that *B* must be "in resonance" with the oscillations in *A*. This is achieved by adjustment of the inductance of *A*, which is simply a matter of selecting the most suitable ground point with the alligator clip *O*. By withdrawing a stream of sparks from the knob *N* to any piece of metal held in the hand this point can be quickly determined, for the sparks are visibly longest when the resonance point has been located. First select the best coil and then adjust the tapping around that particular turn of wire. This method of tuning to resonance is rather like tuning the broadcasting aerial to suit the receiving set. In a darkened room "brush discharges" will be observable at various points requiring more careful insulation. The different nature of brush and spark forms of discharge is readily demonstrated.

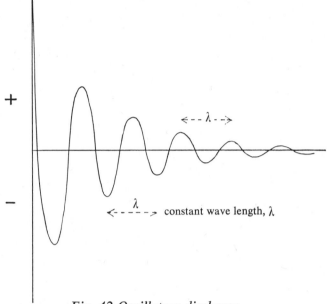

*Fig. 42 Oscillatory discharge*

It should be borne in mind that the discharge from the Tesla coil is unlike that from the induction coil or the model Van de Graaff machine. The Tesla discharge is continuously oscillating in a rapid succession, as Fig. 42 illustrates. Positive-to-negative swings occur at very high frequency, and this is evident in the different appearance of the sparks. They appear to spray out into a multiplicity of flickering tracks through the air.

The frequency in each train of oscillations from the Tesla depends on the capacitance of the Leyden jar $C$ and the inductance $L$ tapped off from the coil (Fig. 43).

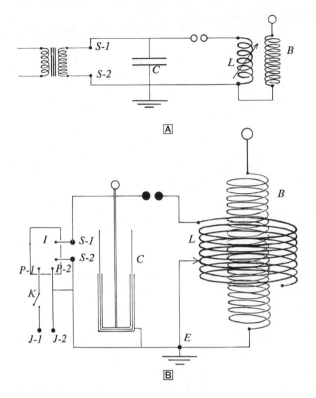

*Fig. 43 The Tesla circuit*

The smaller the capacitance of $C$, the higher the frequency $f$, as is evident from the expression for $f$,

$$f = \frac{1}{2\pi\sqrt{LC}}$$

where $L$ is measured in "henrys" and

$C$ is measured in "farads" and

$f$ is the number of "cycles per second."

Any annoyance to radio and television users by radiation of energy must be avoided, and of course deliberate interference of this sort would be illegal. In this Tesla model we have not specifically added any length of wire to the circuit to act as an aerial, but we must remember that the radio-frequency oscillations generated could dissipate energy into space.

A neon display lamp will light up when held near the Tesla terminal, though not as brilliantly as when used in the orthodox way. Any discharge-tube experiments are best done in the dark.

Entertaining experiments using the Tesla coil may be made with common fluorescent tubes. Discarded lighting tubes 4 or 5 ft. long are fairly readily obtainable nowadays. An incidental word of warning should be given here that powder shaken from broken tubes is highly poisonous.

The residual gas in these tubes is at very low pressure, and sealed to the electrodes at the ends are two starter coils. Switching on the current causes these filaments to heat and vaporize a trace of mercury. The ionized gas contains released electrons and becomes conducting. At this stage the filament current is automatically cut off, and this induces a high-voltage surge in an attached choke coil. This coil therefore acts as a self-starter for the discharge and subsequently limits the current through the gas. The smallness of this current makes the lamps very cheap to run, a point of superiority over the ordinary filament bulb. The light, however, does not come directly from this discharge. A great deal of the energy of the glowing mercury vapor lies in a region outside the range of the visible spectrum. It is ultraviolet, short electromagnetic waves of about 2537 angstrom units length. The bright light results from the interaction of this energy with certain powders deposited on the inner surface of the glass. These materials have the property of absorbing ultraviolet energy and re-emitting it in longer wave lengths as brightly visible light. The cold-fire paints much in evidence at the moment for poster display and similar eye-catching purposes behave in much the same way except that the ultraviolet is supplied by the ordinary illumination. Much research has gone into production of efficient fluorescent powders for the tubes, and color results from different mixtures. Some of the powders used are calcium tungstate, zinc silicate, and cadmium borate, while magnesium is incorporated as an "activator"; but manufacturers have their own "best formulas" for the whitest light and for particular tints.

For our purpose the lamp may be one scrapped as useless, but its vacuum sealing must not be broken. Hold it near the Tesla discharge knob and it will light up. It will not be very bright, but in a darkened room it emits enough light for reading. It is not necessary to hold the actual metallic cap, but when the glass is held anywhere along its length the discharge to the hand (grounded) traverses the low-pressure gas in the tube and the internally deposited powder fluoresces.

# 9 ELECTROLYSIS
## AND ELECTROPLATING

A car with no plated parts would be a dull object; and much of the metal equipment we use in home and office is attractive because of the shining plated finish. Apart from the beauty of the resulting surface, electroplating has the utilitarian virtue of preserving cheaper metals from the ravages of oxidation, tarnishing, rusting, and corrosion. In addition to the more obvious instances of plating around us, electrolytic processes are widely applied in the manufacture of numerous chemicals, producing pure copper and other metals, resurfacing worn parts of machines, duplicating phonograph records, and many other applications.

This chapter suggests some simple experiments in electrochemistry and the deposition of metals.

The subject is not particularly amenable to amateur treatment for two reasons. First, the chemicals needed are almost invariably very poisonous and understandably difficult to obtain. Secondly, the soluble salts one would most like to decompose are those of the precious metals and are correspondingly expensive. A few of the experiments, however, can be done with some of the cheaper salts, such as those of copper, nickel, and chromium, but the work should be done under laboratory conditions and the poisons must be adequately safeguarded.

Before consideration of more involved cases we should examine the conduction of current through water itself. Some simple experiments will contribute toward a clearer understanding of electrolysis, which means the chemical breakdown of a liquid resulting from passage of electricity through it.

Obtain some carbon rods from a discarded two- or three-cell dry battery. Sometimes the carbon rods may be just drawn out, but it is better not to risk pulling off the brass terminal caps. By chiseling or sawing down the cells, the required rods can easily be extracted. The operation is a dirty one but worth while insofar as it will show the construction of the commercial dry cell and the probable reason for its failure. The white corrosion which has destroyed the outer can is zinc

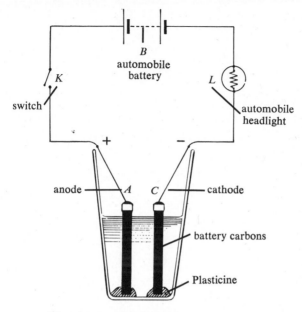

*Fig. 44 Conductivity experiment*

chloride resulting from the interaction of the sal-ammoniac paste with the zinc which formed the negative plate of the cell.

The rods extracted should be cleaned with sandpaper and copper wires soldered onto the caps.

Obtain some distilled water (or de-ionized water), such as garages use for adding to car batteries, and half fill a glass or a jam jar with this. Fix two clean carbon rods (*A* and *C*, Fig. 44) an inch or so apart in the water where they may be held in position with Plasticine. You should be able to obtain Plasticine in any hobby shop or toy store. Join in series with this arrangement a 12-volt car battery, *B*, a 12-volt car headlight, *L*, a key or switch, *K*, and an ammeter if you possess one.

When the circuit is closed the lamp does not light and the ammeter shows no appreciable current to be flowing. Pure water is almost nonconducting. Now stir in about a teaspoonful of battery acid—diluted sulfuric acid—using a plastic spoon for the purpose. At once the bulb lights up and a current is recorded. Instead of acid the addition of common salt, common soda, or sodium sulfate gives similar results. It would seem that the water is rendered conducting by the introduction of the acid or salt or alkali. We shall see later that free ions, charged portions of oxygen and hydrogen atoms, and other groups from the impurity have been released in the solutions, and it is these ions which serve as carriers for streams of electric charges.

The phenomena of electrolysis were studied very carefully by Faraday, and the terminology we still use comes from his descriptions. He was able to enunciate important laws of electrolysis from his quantitative results. The little cell you have made is known as a water voltameter (see Fig. 45). The two rods are called electrodes, the one joined to the positive of the battery being the anode and that on the negative side being the cathode. In case confusion should arise here, be clear that the electrons ( — ) move through the cell from cathode ( — ) to anode ( + ).

With the lamp lighted, examine now the two carbon rods. Bubbles are forming and rising from each electrode. They are, in fact, hydrogen at the cathode and oxygen at the anode, the two gases which, combined, constitute water.

Rearrange the apparatus as follows to collect the gases separately. Heavily paint the cap and the wire from each rod with nail polish and turn the electrodes over as in Fig. 45. Use tap water this time with a little of any acid, even vinegar, in it to increase the ionization and hence the conductance. Invert two test tubes full of water over the rods in the usual manner of gas collection. The water is slowly replaced by the gases evolved as electrolysis proceeds. It will be noticed that the gas at the cathode ($H_2$) comes off at just twice the rate of that at the anode ($O_2$) and this 2:1 ratio of volumes collected is always maintained. To confirm the nature of the two gases, a glowing splint is lighted up by the oxygen and the hydrogen goes off pop or burns with a flame colored yellow by the glass and impurities. Do *not* attempt to ignite the mixed gases, as they explode very violently and such a procedure would invite disaster. Special precautions and apparatus are needed to demonstrate the explosion of even small volumes of the gases. Pure steam, which condenses to a trace of water, results from the recombination of the oxygen and hydrogen, which are entirely used up in the process. Electrolysis has split up the

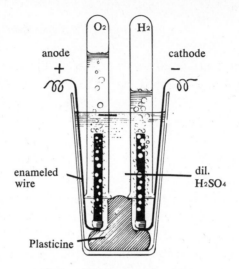

*Fig. 45 Water voltameter*

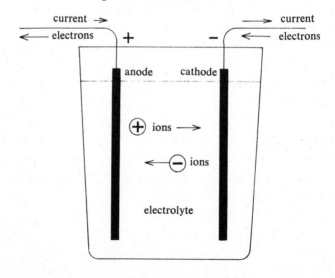

*Fig. 46 Electrolytic cell*

water molecules into their component elements.

At this stage you may care to repeat the experiments with the substitution of alternating current for the direct current of the battery. This is best done with the aid of a small transformer run from ordinary house current. With the 110 volts stepped down to 12 volts the headlight bulb previously used may be included as a series resistance. In this case, reversal of the chemical changes resulting from the rapid current alternation prevents the liberation of gases although the lighted bulb shows current to be flowing. This would serve as a quick test of the d.c. or a.c. nature of a supply.

Having seen the disintegration of water by passage of current through it, we may now turn to the breakdown of metallic salts in solution. You are probably aware that metals dissolved in acids give rise to corresponding salts, many of which are soluble in water. The metal part of the compound is usually freed in a pure state on the negative plate, the cathode of the electrolytic cell. With suitable solutions even alloys such as brass may be similarly deposited. The process is called electroplating; and the object to be plated, which of course must be a conductor, is always made the cathode of the cell. In general, the other electrode, the anode, is a plate of the same metal as that deposited and its transfer across the cell to the cathode is effected by the electrolytic process.

If the anode is extended to both sides of the object to be plated, the deposit is likely to be more uniform in thickness and distribution (see Fig. 47).

For the successful plating of any object certain principles must be observed:

(*a*) The current must be d.c. Storage batteries or dry cells form the most convenient source of this, although a battery charger, if available, would be very effective.

(*b*) The current must be limited to a calculated small value, otherwise a coarse, badly adhering deposit results. An ammeter included in the circuit indicates the current flowing, and it is a great advantage to know this. To vary the current a control rheostat or other means of altering the resistance is also needed. In addition, a voltmeter reading up to about 10 volts connected across the electrodes is very useful.

(*c*) The object to be plated *must* be absolutely clean. Since it must be chemically clean and free from grease, it must not be handled with the fingers after the cleaning process.

(*d*) The composition of the electrolyte requires the chemicals to be measured out carefully.

(*e*) A correct temperature of the plating bath, dependent on the particular solutions used, should be maintained.

As may be imagined, there are many recipes for

plating procedures and tricks of the trade known to the metalplating industry. Some of these have been evolved over the years by craftsmen, and although effective, their exact explanation is not always understood. Modern industrial practice, however, is scientifically controlled and precise.

Usually, objects to be plated are made of metal; but in any case the surface of the material must be conducting and electrically continuous. With regard to its preparation, preliminary treatment with a file and emery cloth may be necessary. Any roughness or irregularity will still show, perhaps more so, in the finished plating. If required in the finished article, a good gloss must be imparted to the original. Efficient removal of grease really needs hot caustic soda treatment, but an ammonia bath is often adequate.

Iron and steel are best cleaned with dilute sulfuric acid, 1 part of acid to 75 of water. The acid cleaning bath for copper and brass is dilute nitric acid, 1 part of acid to 10 of water. A reminder is necessary here. Always add sulfuric acid very slowly to distilled water, stirring and allowing the heat to dissipate. *Never* add water to concentrated sulfuric acid, as a sudden formation of steam may throw acid over you.

You are probably aware, perhaps from dipping a knife blade in copper sulfate solution, that replacement of iron by copper occurs and gives a coating of this metal. It is so thin a layer, however, that it can be regarded as only a surface coloration and not plating proper. As a preliminary small-scale experiment in real plating you should plate an iron nail or screw with copper.

A deep square plastic (polystyrene) food box makes an excellent cell for the purpose, but any glass jar would serve. Hang a bent strip of cleaned copper sheet in the jar to form the anode. Incidentally, scraps of plumbers' copper piping sawed down lengthwise and flattened are a convenient source of sheet copper. Cut a strip of insulator or well-waxed wood to fit over the top of the bath. It will carry the cathode terminal and support the object to be plated (Fig. 47). If the latter is something not easily cleaned with emery— such as a screw—it should be dipped in the dilute sulfuric acid bath already described until all the surface is just lightly etched. The exact strength of the plating solution is not critical, but you should make it up in the proportion of 4 oz. of copper sulfate to 1 oz. of battery sulfuric acid (28%) to 1 pt. of water. A battery attached to the plating bath would produce a deposit of sorts within a few minutes, but you should work more scientifically.

The area of the object should first be estimated. Suppose, for example, you are plating an iron screw and have estimated its area to be approximately 8 cm.$^2$. A suitable current density is 1.0 amp. per dm.$^2$ or 0.01 amp. per cm.$^2$, meaning that we require a current of 0.08 amp. The current is controlled by circuit resistance. If we suppose that a 6-volt battery is our source of current, by Ohm's Law

$$\text{Resistance} = \frac{\text{Electromotive force}}{\text{Current}}$$

which in this case means

$$\text{Whole resistance of circuit} = \frac{\text{Voltage of battery}}{\text{Current through plating cell}}$$

our estimation makes this

$$\frac{6}{0.08} = 75 \text{ ohms}$$

Although the internal resistance of a dry cell might itself amount to several ohms, that of a storage battery would be negligible. Thus the rest of the circuit, plating cell, and any variable resistance should be in the region of 75 ohms. An ammeter in circuit is obviously useful in checking the 0.08-amp. current, but we might dispense with the rheostat if the spacing of the electrodes in the tank can be altered. The closer they are, the less the voltameter resistance and the greater the current.

Do not be tempted to increase the rate of deposition by increasing the current, as this engenders a porous, lumpy deposit of copper which will rub off as soon as the object is removed and handled. It is better to leave the cell set up many hours, perhaps all night, until the required thickness of deposit is attained.

A suitable subject for a first experiment in copper-plating a nonconductor could be a small ivy leaf. Since intricate convolutions are no disadvantage here, one might try a tiny fern leaf, a common weed, or even parsley. Leaves may be dry and pressed, or freshly gathered. Thin down some shellac with alcohol, and after dipping the leaf in the solution shake off any surplus. In a few minutes it will be nearly dry and tacky. At this stage sprinkle it all over with a conductor such as finely powdered graphite or the fine copper bronze dust used in bronze paint. Shaking the tacky specimen in a box containing a little of the dust is effective. Painting with liquid black lead might serve the same purpose, but obviously any insulating base in a paint would not be permissible, since the surface is to be rendered conducting.

Using fine copper wire, tie the specimen to the cathode hook as in Fig. 47. Set up the circuit of Fig. 48 and adjust the rheostat to pass the requisite current.

The drain on the battery (0.08 amp.) is so small that deposition may often be left to proceed for two or three days. If the deposited copper layer is too thin to give adequate strength to the leaf, prolong the plating time and produce a thicker coating. Immediately on removal from the plating bath the fresh copper de-

## TABLE OF WORKABLE PLATING FORMULAS

|   | | Bath | Temperature (°C.) | Current density (amp./cm.$^2$) |
|---|---|---|---|---|
| 1 | *Copper* | 20 gm. $CuSO_4$ | 15 | 0.01 to 0.015 |
|   |   | 38 cm.$^3$ $H_2SO_4$ | | |
|   |   | 1 liter dist. water | | |
| 2 | *Nickel* | 120 gm. $NiSO_4$ | 20 to 30 | 0.005 to 0.01 |
|   |   | 15 gm. $NH_4Cl$ | | |
|   |   | 15 gm. boric acid | | |
|   |   | 1 liter dist. water | | |
| 3 | *Chromium* | Chromic acid 250 gm. liter | 38 | 0.1 amp./cm.$^2$ |
|   |   | 1 liter dist. water (the bath is hot and the anodes are of lead) | | |

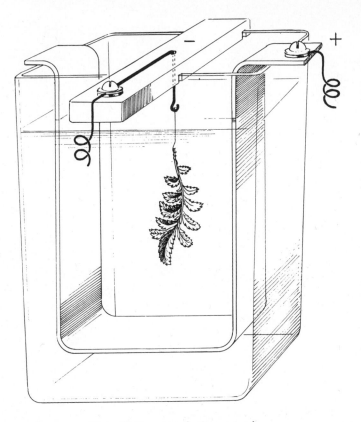

*Fig. 47 Copperplating a leaf*

posit is a beautiful salmon-pink color, but this is quickly lost as the exposed surface tarnishes in air. To retain this attractive color, rinse the leaf quickly in hot water and dry it without overheating. Plunge it in diluted varnish or cellulose acetate to give it a protective coating. Dried while warm, the varnish will not develop a milky opacity. You may then wish to add

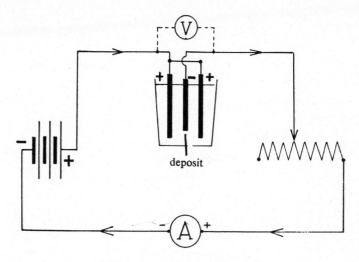

*Fig. 48 The plating circuit*

gem stones or "pearls" to ornament the face. Obtain the requisite finish by burnishing, buffing, or polishing the metal.

The ornament you finally produce may not quite reflect all your expenditure of time and effort, but at least it will be unique. It will certainly lead to appreciation of the perfection of finish achieved commercially in even the cheapest of fashion jewelry.

Great beauty of surface is attained in many common metal products such as car accessories, bathroom fittings, and tableware. Familiar items like cosmetic bottle caps are so lavishly produced and so lightly discarded that we tend to ignore the technical skills to which we owe their profusion. A vast body of knowledge has been built up by the technologists of the metal-finishing industry, and, for the different phases of the work, specially compounded products are marketed by big industrial plating houses.

The chemicals blended are not, however, accessible to the amateur experimenter. As indicated earlier, most plating processes are not possible in the home by reason of the poisonous nature of the electrolytes.

# 10 SOME ELEMENTARY ELECTRONICS

Radio enthusiasts, hams, usually subcribe to magazines which keep them in touch with recent developments and are a source of constructional detail and circuitry. These facilitate the building of receiving sets of special interest. It is not within the scope of this book to elaborate details of receiver or transmitter circuits. Some prior familiarity with cells, resistors, and capacitors must be taken for granted, and it is assumed that the reader is at least conversant with Ohm's Law

$$\text{Current} = \frac{\text{Electromotive force (e.m.f.)}}{\text{Resistance}}$$

This section of the book is therefore limited to building up some basic units and discussing their operation and the function of component parts. The parts are usually easily obtained from radio stores, but items from dismantled sets are often equally serviceable. Once the fundamentals are grasped, more elaborate devices may be tackled and the units described in these pages may be adapted and incorporated into them.

Apart from the reception of broadcasts, there is a very wide field of experiments in electronics. Plenty of scope exists, for example, in the range of devices operable by photo-relay circuits, burglar alarms, baby-tending amplifiers, proximity relays, and so on. Radio control of models is in itself a fascinating field. Anyone who has seen complex sequences of operation performed by models controlled over big distances by variable-frequency transmission must surely have been impressed. Models such as airplanes, boats, and tanks operated by remote control will exhibit behavior seemingly uncanny to the uninitiated. They can actuate rudders and ailerons, change direction and speed, or fire guns at the will of the transmitter operator. While these make fascinating toys, the basic mechanism of control is clearly more important than any complexities of dependent operations, and it is this basis which we hope to clarify. Meanwhile great fun can be derived from making models which exhibit almost human, and occasionally wayward, responses to the wishes of the operator. The items to be described, then, are to be regarded as tools helpful in further electronic development rather than as ends in themselves.

A surprisingly large amount of work can be accomplished using very few factory products, but some, such as microphones, speakers, and tubes, will have to be purchased. Measuring instruments, either separate or multirange, are a great asset, as are signal tracers and cathode-ray oscilloscopes for more advanced work. From the earliest stages, however, enthusiasts should quickly collect a junk-box assemblage of components from broken-down receivers. Resistors and capacitors, fastened by their wire tails to perforated cards, are more conveniently accessible than when scattered through a jumble of parts, and their values, deduced from the color code (see Appendix), should be noted against each component.

The last decade has seen an enormous expansion in the use of transistors, since these tiny devices are, in many instances, capable of replacing more cumbersome vacuum tubes. The necessary power supplies are also comparatively light. The tendency has been to split this branch of physics into vacuum-tube electronics and transistor electronics. For compactness, low weight, and portability generally, transistors have obvious merits, though the student is not usually worried by the size of components. Moreover, a training in vacuum-tube operation is invaluable to the transistor technician, for which reason we shall consider this aspect first.

## A USEFUL POWER-SUPPLY UNIT FOR VACUUM-TUBE CIRCUITS

Radio sets and other devices employing vacuum tubes invariably require a d.c. source providing the positive voltage for the anodes (plates) of the tubes. In addition they need a filament-heating current, usually at 6.3 volts. It is therefore most useful to set up in fairly permanent form a power pack which can be used in conjunction with a variety of circuits constructed later. Besides the variously transformed output voltages, it is useful also to have regular a.c. house-current supply available on panel terminals.

The power unit may be built up conveniently on a panel 12 in. by 8 in. Circuits are often built on metal plates and cased in metal, since most components are readily insulated and wiring can be passed through rubber grommets: the casing forms the ground. It is more advisable, however, to mount the power unit on a panel of good insulator strong enough to carry weighty components like the transformer. A resin-bonded laminated sheet, or thick Masonite, is best for this purpose.

It is suggested that all the necessary components for

the unit be assembled before the panel is marked out or cut. Those required are listed below. Substitution of other types is, of course, permissible provided you know that they will function in an equivalent way.

Transformer. 110- to 120-volt primary input. Secondaries: H.T. 250-0-250 volts at 75 ma.; L.T. 6.3 volts at 2 amp.; etc.

2 selenium-metal rectifiers. 250 volts r.m.s., 250 ma. These are medium-current, high-tension types

2 canned electrolytic double capacitors. 50-50 mfd., 350 volts

Low-frequency smoothing choke. 10 henrys at 90 ma., 285 ohms

Double-pole, double-throw toggle switch

270-ohm, 2-watt resistor (carbon composition)

Pilot bulb. 6.5 volts, 0.3 amp.

7 insulated terminals

Terminal strip. Masonite 8 in. by 1½ in.

Wire and ordinary electrical plug

About 14 nuts, bolts, and washers. $\frac{5}{32}$ in.

Some aluminum strip to make holding angle brackets

In most radio circuits the precise arrangement of components is of some importance because of stray fields and possible interaction, but this does not apply to the power pack. The components should simply be located as conveniently as possible on the panel.

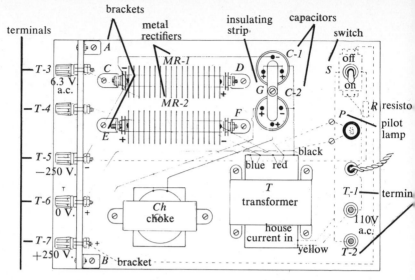

*Fig. 49 Panel of power-supply unit*

Before attempting to explain the electronics involved, we may look at the suggested layout shown in
Fig. 49.

From some ½ -in.-wide strip of heavy aluminum, cut
half a dozen angle brackets with sides about ½ in. and
1 in. long. Drill these to take the ⁵⁄₃₂-in. bolts. Space
out five holes in the terminal strip as shown. Two of
these, *T-3* and *T-4*, are for the 6.3-volt a.c. output,
and the other three are for the high-tension d.c. output. All the terminals used should be well insulated.
If they are of the type intended for metal panels
and fitted with insulators, the holes may have to be of
¼ -in. diameter. Some experimenters prefer to use ba-
nana plugs and fit sockets instead of terminals. The
screw terminals used on this model would also accept
the 4-mm. plugs so useful in experimental work.

Using brackets *A* and *B*, mount the terminal strip 1 in. from one end of the Masonite panel and screw beneath it two strips of wood 12 in. by 1¼ in. in order to give clearance there. The transformer *T* and choke *Ch* will probably be already fitted with brackets. Mark the positions for these and drill the holes required for their holding bolts. The two metal rectifiers *MR-1* and *MR-2* are held by the remaining brackets, *C, D, E,* and *F*. The two double capacitors, *C-1* and *C-2*, are held in place by a single 2½ -in. bolt with an insulating strip, *G*, across the top. Alternatively they could be clamped down horizontally with metal clips. Half-inch holes are drilled for the toggle switch *S* and for the pilot lamp *P*. The pilot lamp is simply pushed through a rubber grommet of suitable size. The bulb contacts are a wire loop and a springy strip screwed beneath the panel. Discarded auto trouble-lights or lanterns provide lots of handy material for such improvisation and a lamp-holder portion might well be adapted here. Terminals *T-1* and *T-2* give the ordinary house current, 110 volts a.c., when the switch *S* is on. A rapid-discharge resistor, *R*, is in circuit when *S* is in the off position. This is simply a safety device to avoid accidental shock from the charged condensers *C-1, C-2*.

Solder the various connecting wires according to the circuit diagram, Fig. 50. If bare wire is used for this, then 1-mm. spaghetti sleeving should be slipped

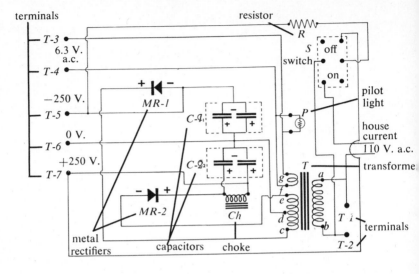

*Fig. 50 Circuit of power-supply unit*

on for insulation. Use a clean, well-tinned soldering iron and be sure that the solder flows on the joint like quicksilver to avoid any possibility of dry joints. Special care is needed in joining up the metal rectifiers and the electrolytic capacitors, since these are polarized; they have marked positive and negative terminals. They will not function and may be destroyed if connected the wrong way around.

The beginner in electronics will realize that ability to read a conventional circuit diagram is essential to rapid progress. The first stage is to become familiar with the symbols; several of these occur in Fig. 50. Fig. 49 is not a circuit diagram, although some wiring is shown, but a plan of components set out on a panel. It shows relative positions of switch, transformer, choke, etc. Again, Fig. 50 is not the best schematic diagram—that is, one of greatest simplification most readily acceptable to a technician. It has been drawn to match more closely the actual layout of components.

Referring to Fig. 50, then, we note that the symbol for a fixed-value resistor is a zigzag line *R*. Capacitors are represented as equal parallel lines *C-1*, *C-2*. The iron-cored transformer *T* has several windings, but three of these are shown in use. The low-frequency choke *Ch* is iron-cored, as indicated by the parallel lines added to the inductance coil. The selenium-metal rectifiers *MR-1* and *MR-2* have positive and negative sides not always so clearly marked as in this instance. Wire junctions are often, but not necessarily, shown with a dot. Mere crossings are indicated by loops.

Do not be alarmed by apparent complexity in a circuit diagram. When once familiar with the symbols of components, various types of tubes, etc., you will quickly learn to read an electronic circuit.

The switch *S* is of the double-pole, double-throw type, which means that it has six isolated contacts. In the on, or down, position the lower vertical side points are joined, while in the up position the upper pairs of side points are joined. Dotted lines are merely component boundaries. Only four of the six contacts happen to be in use here.

Consider the switch in the on position. One side of the a.c. house current is linked with *T-2* and also with the primary winding *b* of the transformer *T*. The other side of the house current goes to *T-1* and to the primary at *a*. *T-1* and *T-2* are convenient panel terminals providing an output of 110 volts a.c. This represents the effective or root mean square value and not the peak value of the voltage swing, which would be about 1.4 times greater. As these power voltages are quite large, it should hardly be necessary to emphasize the extreme importance of insulation and the vital necessity for care in the use of all such models. Make it a rule never to handle the apparatus for alterations without first switching off and also removing the plug from the wall socket. Always check circuits twice before reconnecting. These are sensible precautions which save damage to equipment and danger from shock.

The chief output winding of the transformer is the coil between *e* and *c*, distinguished by red wires. On an a.c. meter these wires would give over 500 volts, nominally 250-0-250 volts when delivering 75 milliamperes. The "0" refers to potential of a center-tap point on the winding. This is taken from a black wire on the point *d*, and it is common practice to ground the center tap.

Two blue wires, from *g* and *f*, are taken from a small winding in which is induced an a.c. voltage

stepped down to less than 7 volts. This is achieved by
having fewer turns on the winding than on the
primary side by a factor of 16. The wire of the small
coil, however, being thicker, can handle the 2 amp. of
current required of it. On the other hand, the large
number of turns in the secondary, *c-e*, necessitates fine
wire; but this, fortunately, has to carry only 0.075
amp. The blue wires give the 6.3 volts, useful for
heating the filaments of indirectly heated tubes. In
these, the electron-emitting cathode is heated by the
proximity of the filament; hence this may be run off
an a.c. supply.

The circuit diagram shows the pilot lamp *P* to be
directly across this 6.3-volt output, which is also taken
to the terminals *T-3* and *T-4*. The immediate illumination of this bulb is a useful indication that the house
current has been switched onto the transformer.

The transformer may also have other secondary
windings giving 5 volts at 2 amp. and 6.3 volts at 1
amp. These wires, brown, white, orange, and violet,
are not being used in the present case, and so their
bare ends are insulated and the wires coiled up neatly.
If desired, of course, they could be taken to appropri-
ately marked binding screws on the panel or terminal
strip.

It is noted that one red 250-volt lead from the
transformer joins the positive side of one stack of
selenium rectifiers *MR-1* and the other one goes to the

negative side of *MR-2*. The function of these units is to pass current only in one direction and therefore pass alternate halves of the voltage swing. The resulting surges of pressure are then smoothed out into a steady d.c. supply by the action of the capacitors and choke. A very rough analogy as suggested in Fig. 51 might be helpful here.

Imagine a to-and-fro pump piston *P*, supplying water to a hose outlet, *O*. Air, compressed in a pressure dome, *C*, maintains the pressure while the piston is doing its return stroke. The narrow pipe *Ch*, somewhat equivalent to the electrical choke, limits the flow so that pressure builds up in *C* and the final output at *O* is steady. Do not fall into the trap of attempting to carry such an analogy too far, but just as the pressure dome momentarily stores water and smooths out the pressure changes, so the capacitors and choke produce a d.c. output. Our electrical counterpart of the pump valves which pass fluid in only one direction consists of the selenium rectifiers; the counterpart to the pressure dome lies in our storage capacitors. The system used here is worth studying. Capacitors, which were at one time rather inappropriately termed condensers, have the property of storing up charge. An enormous variety of different types is made—mica, waxed paper, and metal foil; some flat, some cylindrical. In these, polarity is immaterial, but with the electrolytic type we are using, the polarity of

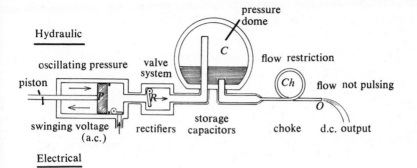

*Fig. 51 Analogy to smoothing*

the plates is very clearly marked and must be strictly observed in wiring. These electrolytics are obtainable in huge capacities of up to 5000 mfd., and the lower range of up to 200 mfd. are designed to stand potentials as high as three or four hundred volts. Those listed for use in our present circuit are of the double type, which means that two capacitors are incorporated in one can. There are three terminals: a common negative tag, black; one positive tag, red; and the other positive, unpainted.

Now the top capacitor, *C-1* in Fig. 50, simply uses the two parts in parallel and could quite well be replaced by a single 100-mfd. capacitor. The lower one, *C-2*, has the choke across the two positive sections. When the voltage swing from the transformer is in the direction to charge up *C-2*, its positive plates produce a potential on *T-7* which may surge as high as 350 volts above the center-tap terminal *T-6*. Similarly, in the reverse sense, the negative side of *C-1*,

when charged, can swing *T-5* 350 volts negative to
*T-6*. *T-7* would then be 700 volts positive to *T-5*,
which is a usefully high potential difference. When
delivering current this potential difference would, of
course, show a considerable fall. If you prefer the use
of four separate capacitors in the positions shown,
there may be some advantage gained in heightened
insulation and less risk of breakdown under accidentally heavy load.

Notice that the circuit given here is a dual-output
device and not the normal type of full-wave rectifier
circuit which would employ four sections of metal
rectifier. It is nevertheless a nicely smoothed output
and forms a very versatile power source which should
prove of value to the electrical experimenter.

## A SIMPLE TEST PANEL FOR TRANSISTORS

Transistors obtained from discarded apparatus and
cheap sources sometimes turn out to be substandard
or useless. It is helpful, therefore, to wire up a little
test panel which, while not giving precise numerical
measurement, at least shows whether the transistors
are usable or not.

Hundreds of different types of transistors are now
marketed, and their characteristics vary within a wide
range according to their intended use. Transistors
now replace tubes in their multifarious duties of rectification, amplification, etc., and a current gain of up

to 100 is common. One should naturally apply voltages below the maxima stated by the makers; this usually means within a relatively narrow range.

The collector leakage current, usually just called $I_{co}$ or leakage, and the current gain, called $B$, are the factors of first importance. While power transistors may be expected to have considerable leakage, that of the silicon type should be negligible. The ohmic resistance of a commonly used p-n-p type, such as a 2N838 or GE-2, would normally be very high. If one intends to use a matched pair of transistors in a given circuit, their leakages and gains should certainly be the same. In investigating this the test panel is especially useful.

The circuitry described is not elaborate enough to allow measurement of transistor parameters, but is about the simplest arrangement likely to be useful to the amateur. It is only suitable for the low-power p-n-p transistors in common use—arrangements for polarity reversal would need to be added to cope with the n-p-n type.

The first requirement is a low-range milliammeter with a full-scale deflection (F.S.D.), preferably in the range 1 to 5 ma. Such meters are usually available at radio surplus shops. Values of resistors to be used in series with the meter would depend on its range, but they may be calculated from Ohm's Law as in the following example:

Assume the transistor has too great a leakage if its resistance (emitter to collector) is less than 4000 ohms. Suppose that we apply a 4.5-volt battery, that the meter itself is 75 ohms, and that we use it in series with a 500-ohm resistor.

Since

$$\text{Current} = \frac{\text{E.m.f.}}{\text{Total resistance}}$$

the current passed $= \dfrac{4.5}{4575}$ amp., or just under 1 ma.

It will be seen that the 500-ohm value passes a current which would show up well on a meter of F.S.D. 2.5 ma. One of F.S.D. 1 ma. or less might need an appropriate shunt to increase its range.

Either mount up the components of the tester in a transparent plastic food box or arrange them neatly on a panel of insulator and make this form the lid of a box.

Relative position of the components is not important, but that shown as front and back views in Fig. 52C and D is convenient. The circuit is shown in Fig. 52B. *A* is a 4.5-volt battery held in position either by a spring or by rubber bands. *P* is a bell-push form of switch. *R* is a 500-ohm resistor which reference to the color code on p. 195 will show to be green, black, brown. *S* is a ¼-megohm resistor (red, green, yellow).

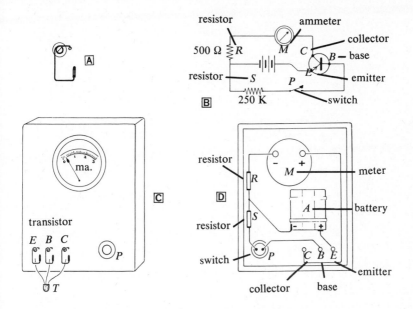

*Fig. 52 Simple test panel for transistors*

For convenience one should be able to attach the transistor quickly and correctly. Spring clips for wire connection can be bought, but springs to hold the tail wires of the transistor are easily made from three 1-in. safety pins. Twist the "safety" end through 90° and make three other right-angle bends as shown in Fig. 52A. The pointed end should pass through the panel and be cut off on the underside to form a "steady pin," while the holding screw passes through the hinge of a safety pin. These spring clips must be clearly marked *E* for emitter, *B* for base, and *C* for collector. They are not evenly spaced: *B* is displaced toward *E*.

This helps to avoid expensive mistakes in connection, since the tail wires are similarly spaced on many transistors. The collector contact is marked with a red spot on some types, and a corresponding spot of nail polish on that clip is helpful.

If both good and faulty samples of transistors are available, the performance of the tester may be quickly demonstrated. Make the following tests:

(1) Attach the transistor wires to the current clips and watch the meter. It may register 0.2 to 0.5 ma.; in general, the smaller the leakage, the better the transistor. No reading at all may indicate an open circuit—perhaps a complete break or a burnt-out unit. The resistance may be too low, shown by too great leakage, and if the current exceeds about 1.25 ma., the transistor is poor. A short circuit would flick the needle right across the meter scale, but with only momentary connection, the 500-ohm resistor should prevent damage.

(2) Warm the transistor by holding it between thumb and forefinger. This causes a drop in its resistance, which occurs more quickly if the sample is metal-cased than if glass-encapsulated. With increased leakage the current may build up to 1 ma. or more. Allow the transistor to cool again, and the fall of the meter reading will show the resistance to be reverting to its normal high value. This experiment emphasizes the sensitivity of transistors to heat and explains the

necessity for the heat-dissipation devices, called heat sinks, often used with them. Leakage current can increase seven times for a rise from 25° C. to 45° C., and of course any considerable rise in temperature will destroy a germanium transistor.

(3) The next test, that for gain, requires closure of the switch $P$. The effect of this is to apply a negative potential to $B$ relative to $E$ by connecting the 4.5 volts through the 250-K. resistor $S$. This current through $B$ is minute, perhaps 0.02 ma., but the magnified effect on the collector current is considerable, and this is shown additively on the meter. If this gain causes 1.0 ma. to flow, the value of $B$ will be about 1.0/0.02 or 50. An appreciable increase of current should thus become visible on the meter. According to circumstances this jump might be from 0.2 to 1.5 ma. and would indicate satisfactory gain in the transistor. $P$ should not be kept depressed longer than necessary because of the possibility of overheating leading to the thermal runaway noted above. It is worth remembering that this gain, the current amplification factor $B$ of the transistor, is the ratio

$$\frac{\text{Change in emitter current}}{\text{Change in the base current}}$$

A gain of over 30 is quite usual for audio transistors. This is one factor which makes the device so valuable as an amplifier of radio signal strength.

Sometimes a specimen which is worthless from the "triode" standpoint may still be usable as a "diode," but of late, transistors have become sufficiently cheap and plentiful to justify scrapping any which function incorrectly.

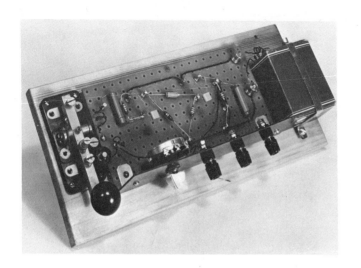

## 11  MAKING AN
##     AUDIO-OSCILLATOR

The diaphragm of a loudspeaker or of a telephone would be mechanically incapable of vibrating at vast frequencies such as millions of cycles per second (c.p.s.), and even if it could do so the human ear would not detect the sound.

An audio-oscillator produces fluctuations of current and corresponding vibrations of the diaphragm of headphones or speaker that lie within the range of audible notes. If they were too slow, less than about 20 c.p.s., the buzz could hardly be called a note; and at the other end of the scale, the upper limit of audible frequencies would be about 30,000 c.p.s. Oscillators

*145*

designed to produce electromagnetic waves of extremely high frequency are used for wireless transmission, since these radio-frequency waves have the capacity for traveling immense distances. At the other extreme an oscillator can be made to produce very slow ticks like those of a metronome.

At the moment we are concerned with the intermediate range of audio-oscillations—20 c.p.s. to 30,000 c.p.s. Several forms of circuit, tube- or transistor-operated, can be made to generate such oscillations. The particular frequency range we desire to cover is governed by the actual components used, and these must be suited to the vacuum tubes or transistors in the circuit.

Without going into detail, it may be stated that for a loop containing an inductance coil $L$ and a capacitor $C$ in series (see Fig. 53A), there is a natural frequency to which it is particularly responsive or resonant. This number of c.p.s. varies inversely with the square root of the product of $L$ and $C$. Thus, high frequencies require small values of $L$ and $C$, while low frequencies require large values of $L$ and $C$.

The two adjacent drawings, Fig. 53A and B, are intended to make comparison of the use of the vacuum tube and the transistor in their somewhat analogous roles. Look first at Fig. 53A. It illustrates a common type of triode tube circuit called the Meissner Oscillator. Any oscillations set up in the $L$-$C$ loop

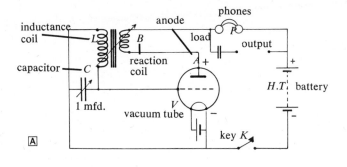

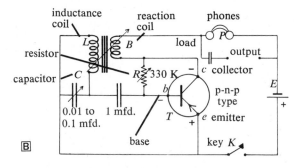

*Fig. 53 Analogous transistor and vacuum-tube oscillators*

die away unless energy is fed back to maintain them. Notice that the fluctuations of potential in this circuit are applied to the grid of the tube and that they trigger off tube currents. These draw energy from the high-tension battery *HT* and give magnified fluctuations of potential across the load. Now a small portion of this energy passes back by way of the reaction coil *B* to the inductance *L* by electromagnetic induction. The feedback energy is in phase with the existing oscillations and maintains them at a constant level instead of permitting them to die out. The amount of energy so returned is controlled by the degree of coupling between the coils *B* and *L*. That the coupling is variable is indicated by the arrow drawn on the transformer. If a small intertube transformer were used with a coil ratio of about 3:1, the coupling would in this case be fixed. Coupling could be controlled by sliding *B* off a straight transformer core or by moving a soft-iron keeper from a ring core. This same method of reaction is used for boosting up a small input signal to the grid of a detector tube as a volume control in some radio receivers.

Apart from the winding *B*, the only load shown lies in the impedance of the headphones. The note is heard in these phones and oscillation continues as long as the key *K* is closed. This is useful for Morse code practice.

At first sight Fig. 53B, with a transistor in place of the tube, shows a circuit very similar to that in A, but important differences are soon evident. First, we have no high-tension battery because, unlike the vacuum-tube anode in A, the transistor requires no high voltage. Secondly, we notice that with this p-n-p type of transistor the emitter, *e*, is on the positive side and the collector, *c*, is made negative; whereas in vacuum-tube circuitry the negative side is usually grounded, in transistorized work the positive side is normally grounded. The p-n-p, the commonly used type of transistor, is drawn in the circuit of Fig. 53B, but the analogy with the tube would have been even more striking had we shown an n-p-n type, since the collector would then have been positive and the emitter negative.

Compared with emission of electrons from cathode to anode of a tube the behavior of a transistor is somewhat complicated and it is impossible to include its description here. Readers interested should consult a work entirely devoted to radio.

Very briefly, a transistor is a back-to-back pair of junction diodes, germanium layers with a sandwiched common base, a paper-thin layer of germanium. The property by which transfer of electrons and positive holes takes place is given by other trace elements—arsenic, indium, boron, etc., impurities deliberately fused into the outer layers. Useful attributes of tubes—rectification, amplification, and oscillation—can all be simulated by transistors, and their minuteness makes them an invaluable contribution to recent developments of science such as computers and rocketry.

The polarity of the three layers is of prime importance in wiring a transistor. For this reason the beginner should observe carefully the direction of the arrow in the symbol which defines the type of transistor. One directed from emitter to base signifies the p-n-p type, while the reverse means the n-p-n type.

A helpful rule regarding polarity of connection is:
For n-p-n: emitter *negative* relative to the collector.
For p-n-p: emitter *positive* relative to the collector.
You will see from Fig. 53B that the base *b* is also biased negative, through the rheostat *R*, and this controls the current passed to the collector.

On first trying out a circuit like Fig. 53B you may be disappointed at finding no oscillation. This may be because the pulses in coil *B* are canceling instead of augmenting those in *L*; so in the first place try reversing the connections to *B*.

A different type of oscillating circuit, more akin to a tube multivibrator, is the model we now suggest making up in transistorized form. Examine the circuit of Fig. 54. The two amplifying transistors *T-1* and *T-2* are linked by a resistance-capacitance mesh. *T-2* feeds back energy to *T-1*, so that they are energized alternately. The pitch of the note generated is controlled by several factors but mainly by the size of the capacitor *C-1*. This determines the general range of frequency, but the rheostat *R* itself gives smooth variation over quite a wide range for any one capacitor. When a value of 0.001 mfd. is inserted as *C-1*, and *R* is moved to its lowest setting, the frequency of the author's model rises right out of the audio range.

Fig. 55 and the photograph at the beginning of this chapter show a scheme for laying out the components

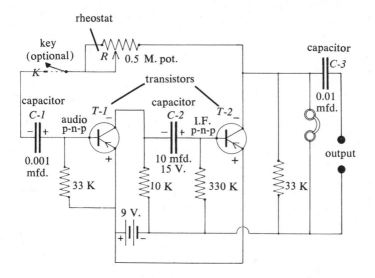

*Fig. 54 Circuit of transistorized*
*variable-frequency audio-oscillator*

in which the wiring is all on top of a piece of pegboard. This was done for clarity, but obviously a closer packing and subpanel wiring would result in a very compact unit.

A 4½-volt battery from a lantern or an auto trouble-light is a source of power that will last for a long time, and the loudness is dependent on the voltage of the battery used. There are many uses for the device. As arranged in the photograph, with a Morse key attached, it makes a sounder for code practice and any homemade spring contact or push-button switch can be utilized as a key for this purpose.

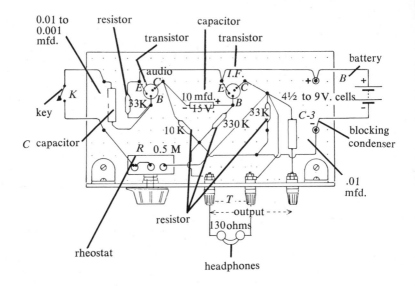

*Fig. 55 Oscillator components on pegboard*

The phone terminals give sufficient output for a loudspeaker or enough to work numerous sets of headphones, especially if the battery voltage is brought up to 9 volts. The output terminals provide an audio signal useful for testing the behavior of audio-amplifiers. For radio and television servicing the unit might form a useful signal tracer. In this connection, the purpose of the 0.01-mfd. blocking condenser *C-3* is to transmit the audio-oscillations while preventing any d.c. from the set under test from passing back into the unit.

As an oscillator for standardized frequencies a dial beneath the rheostat knob might be calibrated, but variable factors such as battery voltage and phone resistance would have to be carefully stabilized.

Parts used in building this oscillator are listed below, but components already in your possession might well be substituted.

Base panel
Terminal strip
Turret tags. Terminals. Knob
4½ -volt battery or a 9-volt grid-bias battery
1 pair of headphones (60- to 250-ohm range)
1  0.001-mfd. capacitor (and other substitute values
   if possible)
1  0.01-mfd. capacitor
2  33-K., ½ -watt resistors
1  10-K., ½ -watt resistor
1  330-K., ½ -watt resistor
1  ½ -megohm potentiometer
1  10-mfd. 15-volt subminiature electrolytic capacitor

The assembly is obvious from Fig. 55. The base was a pegboard sheet 8 in. by 4 in., to the front edge of which was bracketed a plain strip of Masonite or Bakelite 2 in. deep. This front panel carried the output terminals and control rheostat for altering the pitch of the note. The rheostat was the ½ -megohm potentiometer listed above, with the slider and one end strapped together as shown. The black spots in the diagram are anchoring points for soldering. These are

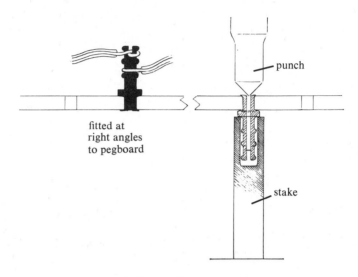

fitted at
right angles
to pegboard

punch

stake

*Fig. 56 Inserting a turret tag*

the very convenient turret tags. They are easy to fix in the perforations by tapping the underside with a punch while holding the tag vertical in a hollow "stake" (see Fig. 56). Being ready-tinned, these little brass posts are easily soldered with the touch of a hot bolt. Do not, however, forget to solder the transistor tail wires rapidly, holding the wire with cold pliers near the actual transistor. This prevents damage by heat.

The circuit described will almost certainly operate satisfactorily since a fair latitude in component values is allowable. Probably the most suitable transistors would be an RCA SK3005 or a GE-1 PNP on the right and an RCA SK3004 or GE-2 PNP on the left.

Do not be dissuaded from setting up a circuit because exact types quoted are unavailable. Try out what you have. There are many substitute types for any transistor, and also large variations in characteristics which are attributable to differences in factory production. Cheap transistors, manufacturers' surplus, often work as well as expensive ones, though perhaps without the same guarantee of success.

## USING AN OSCILLOSCOPE

A cathode-ray oscilloscope (C.R.O.) is not described as a project in this book, but it is one of the most useful tools an electronics engineer can possess, since it provides visual evidence of otherwise hidden conditions.

A visit to research rooms or engineering laboratories discloses scientists working on a great variety of diverse topics; many, if not most of them, are using C.R.O.'s for the display and photography of phenomena which are translatable into readily examined electrical impulses.

Like a television set, a C.R.O. incorporates a cathode-ray tube, and this exhibits the behavior of an electron beam moving under the joint influence of two sets of changing electric potentials, one vertical and the other horizontal.

As C.R.O.'s are so widespread and versatile, the young physicist should endeavor to construct his own oscilloscope. This is much better than buying one ready-made, and the task is not difficult for the experimenter who can read a circuit diagram, is neat-fingered, and can solder connections. Material from scrapped TV sets is often available at radio junk shops. It is a pity that this is its last resting place, since it is often finely and expensively manufactured and invaluable to the experimental physicist. If acquisition of such material is not feasible, you can buy a kit and have the fun of making up your own model. It will be cheaper than a factory model, with the added advantage that you will soon know its circuitry "inside out" as well as its little idiosyncrasies!

On both bought and homemade instruments, panel knobs control the beam in respect to its intensity, focus, vertical and horizontal position, frequency, sweep, and other features. The electrical phenomena to be examined are made to move the beam vertically, and this, combined with its horizontal travel, displays the characteristics of the input. The oscilloscope makes possible a more detailed examination of our audio-oscillator, and it may be of interest to look at tests made on the model described in these pages. Even if at this stage you do not possess your own oscilloscope, it may be possible to borrow one for examination of your tone generator.

Switch on the C.R.O.; its pilot lamp should indicate this by lighting. As with a TV set, allow a minute or so for warming up and a spot or horizontal trace should appear. Centralize this with the X- and Y-shift controls. Adjust the focus and brilliance knobs. Stray pickup may give a wavy line input, but with the lowest time-base frequency setting, the spot should move steadily from left to right, flicking back to the left after each displacement.

It is usually advisable to include isolating capacitors of 0.01 mfd. in leads from the work you are examining to the input terminals of the oscilloscope, especially if house-current voltages are involved.

Probably your first experiments will be to display the 60-c.p.s. wave form of the house-current supply and this may be stepped down through a transformer to some lower voltage (see Fig. 57). If the time-base frequency is adjusted to 30 c.p.s., two almost complete sine waves are visible on the screen (Fig. 57B). Slower base speeds give more waves in each stroke, these being progressively narrower (Fig. 57C). Adjust the brilliance so that the "fly-back" is barely visible. Look for wave distortion caused by accidentally introduced harmonic frequencies (Fig. 57D).

Simple inductance-capacitance oscillations of audio-frequency are pure sine waves and give characteristically pure notes like a lightly struck tuning fork, but added harmonics give a particular quality or "timbre" to the sound and the waves are more

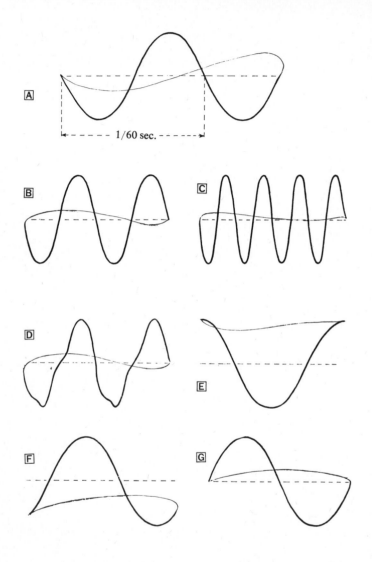

Fig. 57 Some simple wave displays

complex, as in Fig. 57D. Harmonics show up better if you use a base sweep of wide amplitude and only a single wave. As might be expected, reversal of the output connections as applied to the Y-plates in each case merely inverts the picture displayed. One must become familiar with the wave-form variations, such as these, imposed by the manner in which the C.R.O. itself is used. Even the same wave looks deceptively different as a result of phase shift, as may be seen in the single sine wave shown in Fig. 57E, F, and G.

Connect the output terminals of your generator to the amplified input sockets of the C.R.O. These are the work terminals or the Y-plates of the tube which produce the vertical movement. Then adjust the time-base frequency, on the X-plates, to a suitable value to produce two or three steady wave forms. The picture should be easily stabilized by careful adjustment, but increasing. the degree of synchronization may help if a synchronized control is fitted.

The first tests with the oscillator described were made with a pair of 130-ohm headphones left connected across the appropriate terminals *T* in Fig. 55, and so forming a load. The fact that the output terminals were joined to the C.R.O. meant that similar potentials fed to the oscilloscope were transmitted through the 0.01-mfd. blocking condenser in the oscillator.

The 0.001-mfd. capacitor at *C-1* (Fig. 54) gave

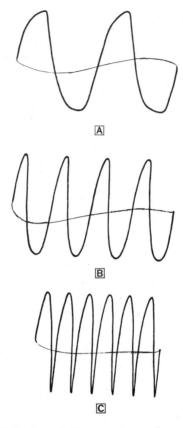

*Fig. 58 Rising-pitch notes from the oscillator*

fairly high notes, and it was useful to be able to hear
these as well as see the oscillation pattern. At different
points of the rising scale typical wave forms were of
the shapes shown in Fig. 58A, B, and C respectively.

With a 0.01-mfd. capacitor added in parallel to
*C-1*, lower notes resulted and more harmonics

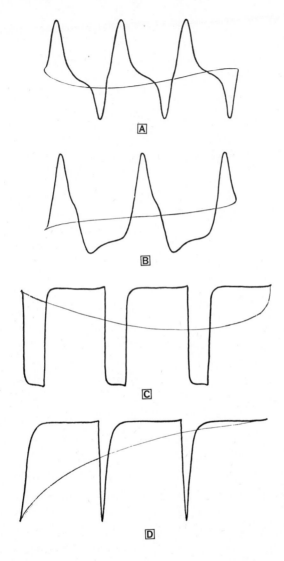

*Fig. 59 Other wave forms from the oscillator*

appeared in the waves as in Fig. 59A and B. It will be realized that the headphone load is in itself a complex system of inductance and resistance and also that peculiar mechanical resonances occur in phone diaphragms at particular frequencies. Moreover, the two phones interact with each other to produce spurious effects which disappear when the phones are isolated. The interaction can cause a sudden jump to a new frequency note. These peculiarities due to the headphones were removed by substituting a purely resistive load across *T*, Fig. 54. The resistance was progressively increased up to 5000 ohms, and it was seen that the amplitude of the wave built up from a small value at 30 ohms to a maximum at about 2000 ohms and then diminished again. In the region of 200 ohms a good square wave of short pulse duration became evident.

Square waves of even better form resulted from taking oscillations between the collector of the left-hand audio transistor and the left-hand phone terminal (Fig. 55)—that is, across the 10-K. resistor. Using this tapping and the 2000-ohm resistive load, a sharply peaked squarish wave resulted; it looked like a differentiated square wave with its positive half-cycles suppressed (Fig. 59C and D).

Checking even as simple a model as our audio-frequency generator will give some impression of the potentialities of the oscilloscope as a tool. Traces which result from different pieces of electronic equipment are of incredible variety, and as scope for experiment is endless it is evident that early familiarity with the instrument is time well spent.

# 12 A WILSON CLOUD CHAMBER

With C. T. R. Wilson's cloud chamber, as with many fundamental discoveries, the associated mental ingenuity and depth of vision seem far to outstrip the simple phenomena and the primitive apparatus used. The cloud chamber was a device for observing and demonstrating the behavior of some of the basic units of all matter generally called fundamental particles.

Cloud chambers based on Wilson's simple idea have played a major part in the discovery of positrons, mu-mesons, and the strange particles recently added to the ever-growing family of recognized units. The minute order of size of molecules and atoms (to say nothing of their constituent particles) is such that man has no hope of ever seeing them directly, since they are much smaller than the wave length of light itself.

A distant airplane may be a speck too small to be noticed, and yet it can give rise to a vapor trail which is very conspicuous. The track betrays the direction and speed of the plane. On a diminutive laboratory scale this is just what Wilson did in order to detect the presence and behavior of speeding atomic particles. Similar and even more useful methods have been devised recently. One method uses laminated blocks of photographic plates, while others, known as bubble chambers, use liquids at their boiling temperature; but Wilson's original method is of such historic importance and yet so simple that we can benefit by imitating it in the way described here.

Usually the air in a room is by no means saturated with water vapor; it is above the temperature at which it displays condensation. (If it were saturated, one would find the air unpleasantly humid to breathe; the fern house in a botanic garden illustrates this. Imagine the room steadily cooled down until a temperature is eventually reached at which the air becomes saturated. This is called the dew point. Now any slightly colder surface introduced at this stage clouds over with deposited moisture. At this or lower temperature, the humidity would be 100% and a cloud of minute water droplets would materialize. In this critical condition, however, their formation may be greatly delayed if the air is very clean and free from suitable nuclei. Electrically charged particles such as ions of gas are nuclei which can trigger off this condensation of vapor.

Picture a charged particle such as a helium nucleus, carrying positive charge, racing through the saturated air at rapid speed. It leaves a vapor trail—a line of condensed water-molecule groups which, when brightly illuminated, clearly defines its track. The streak of light, seen or photographed against a dark background, persists for a short time before vanishing. This is the principle behind the cloud chamber to be constructed.

These are the essential requirements for the cloud chamber:

(*a*) A source of particles capable of ionizing the air by impact—for example, a speck of radioactive material which spontaneously emits them. The most readily available source may be a chip of radioactivated paint from the dial of an old alarm clock.

It will be realized that even minute but concentrated radioactive sources can be very dangerous to health and strict supervision of their availability is enforced. It is therefore improbable that any pure source will be within the reach of the amateur. Quite rightly, stringent regulations surround the possession and storage of such material, and it is normally kept in massive lead blocks which screen the person from harmful radiation. As a solid source of radioactive substance for the cloud chamber the writer used luminous paint scraped from the hands and dial of an old alarm clock, the figures of which glowed constantly in the dark. All luminous paint is not necessarily radioactive; some just fluoresces for a time after exposure to bright illumination. Luminous buttons are also sold which are radioactive—though not, of course, sufficiently so to be a menace to health.

(*b*) Air saturated with water or vapor of other suitable liquid. Denatured alcohol or grain alcohol, which vaporizes at about 78° C., may be used in solution in water on a pad which saturates the air in the chamber.

(*c*) Mechanism for momentarily chilling below the dew point. The temperature drop can be attained by the use of dry ice (solid $CO_2$), but it is not always easily obtainable; instead we propose to chill the air by its momentary expansion, the method adopted by Wilson. One quite effective way of achieving sudden expansion in a small vessel is simply to attach it to a bicycle pump in which the cup washer of the plunger has been reversed. An energetic withdrawal stroke of the pump handle then produces the required chilling in the observation chamber.

(*d*) Absence of turbulence in the vapor; otherwise the true form of the trails is masked or confused. Perforated baffles prevent swirling of the air during expansion.

(*e*) Good side-illumination of the container. A well-placed 60-watt bulb provides sufficient illumination for direct viewing, and a projector beam makes photography of the trails possible.

Wilson himself spent many hours perfecting a glass-and-metal piston arrangement which would suddenly increase the volume of the glass vessel in a ratio of about 3:4, and his model was not much larger than the one now suggested. Later models have varied enormously in size and in experimental range. For example, the Centre Européen pour la Recherche Nucléaire (CERN) at Geneva runs one with a volume of 1 cu. m., and this can be pressurized to 100 atmospheres, but our more modest effort will be the size of a 1-qt. mayonnaise jar.

Obtain some empty mayonnaise jars with screw caps; wider jars would be even better. Successfully adapted, only two are really needed, but spares to

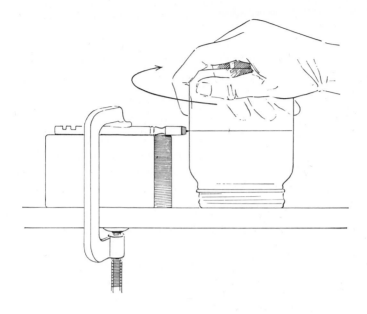

*Fig. 60 Using the glass cutter*

allow for accidental miscutting are useful. Clamp a
glass cutter on top of a wooden block at a height of 2¼
in., as shown in Fig. 60, and with firm pressure rotate
the jar against the diamond or cutter wheel so that a
level scratch encircles the jar.

Use the red-hot Nichrome wire method to lead a
crack around the scratch. Despite care in this
operation, some jars are of such uneven thickness that
the split may not be perfectly level. Select the two best
efforts and either grind the edge flat on the side of an
emery wheel rotating in a lathe or rub down the split
surfaces on a sheet of coarse emery cloth laid flat on a

board. Round off the sharp edges to avoid cutting the rubber-sheet closure. The bases of the jars, similarly smoothed down on emery, make useful dishes for other experiments.

Next, hold the edges of the top surfaces of the two jar lids together and perforate the double-thickness disk with a ring of $\frac{3}{16}$-in. holes. Then solder them together to make an airtight junction unit as shown in Fig. 61A. It is better to make the perforations first, as this avoids blowholes in the soldered edge due to expanding air.

The upper inverted jar $A$, in Fig. 61B, closed by a transparent plate of Lucite, $B$, on top, forms the actual expansion chamber. The lower one, $C$, is a variable-volume chamber closed with a sheet of rubber, $M$, of about the thickness and flexibility of motorcycle inner tube. Bent over the edge of the jar the sheet tends to wrinkle, but the sealing must be made perfect. The method adopted to ensure this is to place one broad rubber band around the glass and another outside the sheet, and then clamp around the whole a band of metal, $D$, like a Terry clip.

The diaphragm is carried up and down by a plunger, $E$, formed from rounded hardwood disks screwed together and sandwiching the rubber between. The two portions of the plunger may be turned on a lathe and should be about an inch smaller in diameter than the jar. Cut a slot in the rod of the

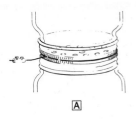

**A**

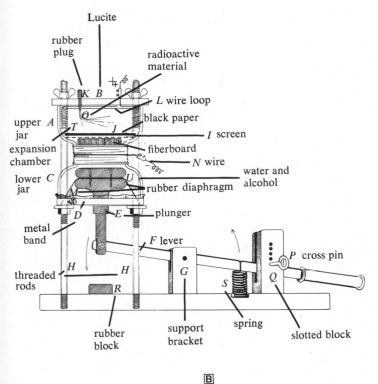

Lucite

rubber
plug

radioactive
material

*K* *B*

*L* wire loop

upper *A*
jar

*O*

black paper

*T*

*J*

*I* screen

expansion
chamber

fiberboard

*N* wire

lower *C*
jar

*U*

water and
alcohol

rubber diaphragm

*M*

*D*

*E*

plunger

metal
band

*F* lever

*P* cross pin

threaded
rods

*H*

*H*

*G*

*Q*

*R*

*S*

rubber
block

support
bracket

spring

slotted block

**B**

*Fig. 61 The cloud chamber mechanism*

mushroom-shaped lower piece to take the hinged lever illustrated in Fig. 61B. Make this lever, *F*, from a strong metal bar pivoted edgewise in a supporting bracket, *G*. For more comfortable operation, the lever may be extended into a wooden or rubber handle.

The double glass vessel was, in the author's model, covered by a ¼-in -thick Lucite plate, *B*, 4 in. square. Care was taken to avoid scratches on this; the protective backing paper was not removed until all cutting and drilling were finished. Corner holes were drilled to take $\frac{5}{16}$-in. fine-threaded rods, *H*. Four lengths of this $\frac{5}{16}$-in. steel rod were obtained from a hardware store, together with wing nuts and ordinary nuts and washers to fit.

Make the baseboard of the model from a block of hardwood about 6 in. by 12 in. by ¾ in. and screw the studding vertically into the base so as to surround the expansion vessels. Cut a metal base plate or ring to support the lower rubber-covered vessel at the right height; the plate is supported on nuts and washers about 2 in. up the rods. The Lucite viewing plate is clamped onto the top chamber by four wing nuts as shown in the photograph.

The downward stroke of the plunger is speeded by a powerful spiral spring, *S*, beneath the lever bar and, manually, the handle and lever give a mechanical advantage of about 2:1. After slow depression of the handle a cross pin, *P*, is inserted in a suitable stop-hole in the slotted block of wood *Q*. When the pin is withdrawn, the plunger falls through its permitted drop in a fraction of a second, causing sudden expansion of the air. The diaphragm drops below the base of the jar; control of the actual distance is effected either by resetting the nuts on the rods or, more easily, by selecting the lever stop-hole which gives the optimum results in practice.

Besides this expansion control, the total air volume in the vessel is altered by the quantity of liquid contained in the lower portion. A block, made from ½-in.-thick perforated disks of fiberboard, is jammed into the necks of the jars, and this also reduces the permanent volume. The top of the fiber block is covered by a disk of perforated zinc or a piece of screen, *I*, and this is faced with a blotter which has been soaked with India ink and then dried. It forms a dense black background for viewing vapor tracks. The edges of the fiberboard and other disks are serrated with a round file to provide air vents, and a wire electrically connects the screen with the metal lids of the jars.

With the plunger in the raised position a mixture of half-and-half denatured alcohol and water is introduced to fill the lower section. This soaks the fiberboard, which becomes the source of saturated vapor. The ratio of alcohol to water does not appear to be at all critical in practice.

Two small holes for insertions into the expansion chamber are drilled near the sides of the Lucite cover plate. One hole takes a rubber plug through which passes a short wire, and on the tip of this wire is cemented the spot of radioactive material. Alternatively the wire can form an extension on a screw, *K*, which goes through the hole in the Lucite. Pass a copper wire through the other hole and shape it into ring *L* beneath the cover plate. Make sure the wire is rigid and its entrance gastight, sealing with epoxy cement if necessary.

A wire, *N*, is also soldered to the metal caps of the jars in order to apply a voltage between the base and the copper wire ring near the top. One purpose of this is to clear the chamber of condensation droplets and charged particles before each expansion experiment. It will be seen from Fig. 61B that the strong spiral spring *S* is compressed when the handle is lowered, and this spring counteracts the inertia of the lever and plunger when released by withdrawal of the cross pin *P*. Otherwise they would have to be made very light to speed the expansion process, which must be as rapid as possible (and adiabatic) to give the maximum temperature drop. A block of rubber, *R*, acts as a buffer directly beneath the plunger.

To proceed with an experiment, after introducing the alcohol solution, stick a speck of the radioactive material *O* to the tip of the pin *K*. In order to sweep the chamber free of ions and droplets, a high-tension source is now required. Any pressure over about 120 volts d.c. will serve for this; even a worn-out H.T. battery might give the accelerating potential needed since we do not propose to draw any current. The high-tension terminals of the power supply unit described in Chapter 10 may be effectively brought into use here. Preferably, tap off the voltage from a potentiometer arrangement on the output—and in any case, for safety, include a high resistance. Join the positive side of whatever source you have decided to use to $L$ and ground the negative side to the wire $N$. This should clear the air in the chamber of any mistiness. Press down the handle and lock the compression with the cross pin $P$. Withdraw $P$ and observe the vapor trails originating at $O$. Two distinct types may be visible. The straight and sharp white streaks are derived from alpha particles, while thinner, longer ones result from beta particles. The latter may also persist for an instant after the alpha tracks have faded out.

A thorium salt (for example, thorium hydroxide) is obtainable, and this makes a useful source for expansion-chamber experiments. A whole series of radioactive derivatives results from the decay of thorium, and nothing we can do will alter this rate of decay. The first stage takes hundreds of millions of years, but on the other hand some stages take fractions of a second. Radon is a gas formed as an intermediate stage before the final stable state of thorium D is reached. The half-life of radon is 54.5 seconds. Traces of this gas are soon present in the air in a bottle of thorium salt, and such air can be squeezed into the cloud chamber from a plastic bottle. The expansion shows numerous straight alpha-particle tracks scattered throughout the chamber. These experiments require replacement of the specimen pin *K* by a rubber tube and pinch clip so that the activated air can be injected into the chamber just prior to expansion.

Although the results of this experiment are not spectacular, a thrill arises from the knowledge that the experiment is following up modern work, and this is a good starting point for further experiment. Photographers will wish to obtain permanent records of the tracks. This is not too difficult, using a short-focus lens, dark background, and strong lighting of the expansion chamber. A method can be devised whereby the expansion stroke—the end of the piston drop—also actuates the camera shutter. Any delay in making the exposure will result in fuzzy tracks, since they quickly disperse, but with correct timing the traces should be bright and sharp.

A further step with this simple apparatus would be to attempt curving the tracks in a powerful magnetic field. This involves designing a coil to surround the chamber, and equipment to pass a heavy surge of current around the coil during the expansion. Among other adaptations, the steel studding supports and tin lid junction piece would have to be replaced by nonmagnetic material. Alpha-particle (helium-nucleus) tracks would be curved in one direction, while beta-particle (electron) tracks would curve in the opposite sense by interaction of the moving charges with the vertical magnetic field.

A prolific mass of data has stemmed from track experiments in recent years and a multitude of new particles, diverse in nature, mass, speed, charge, and spin, have been discovered. The old proton-electron simplicity of the atom of early days has been dispelled forever and replaced by an edifice of apparent complexity. The nature of our material world will not be understood until physicists have further resolved these mysteries.

# 13 RELAYS AND REMOTE CONTROL

A fairly common electrical problem is that of remote control of a circuit. Methods of coping with this may be classed under three heads:

(*a*) Wired relay circuit

(*b*) Light- or photocell-controlled relay

(*c*) Radio-controlled relay

The first method may be applied to the case of a circuit carrying large power, which it is desired to operate indirectly from a distance. The need for this stems from several causes, such as the safety factor, inaccessibility, voltage loss in the lead, high frequency of the main circuit, all reasons making direct control inadvisable. A simple solution is to employ a second-ary, low-power, and therefore safe, circuit to operate the switching of the main one.

A straightforward illustration of this lies in using an electromagnetic relay worked by a small battery to open or close the circuit carrying power from house current. Such a device may be constructed without much difficulty, especially as the electromagnet from an old bell or buzzer may not be too hard to find. Fig. 62A shows the principle involved. When the key *K* is closed, the electromagnet *EM* pulls in its armature, which in turn operates the electric contacts. These may be of platinum or nonoxidizable metal and designed to handle 5 amp. or more at 110 volts. As shown in the diagram, contact *C* is not actually in use, but this is the normally closed (or *NC*) position. Closure of *D*, the normally open (or *NO*) contact, occurs with the electromagnetic pull, and this may be effected by a small current of a few milliamperes, provided the electromagnet resistance is high and the contact gaps are diminutive.

A strong electromagnet may be capable of moving its armature a distance of two or three millimeters in order to operate a mechanical on-off switch by successive pulls. One is familiar with alternately open-ing and closing switches in the push-switches of some table lamps, but a device requiring smaller power to operate it is shown in Fig. 62B. *EM* is the electro-

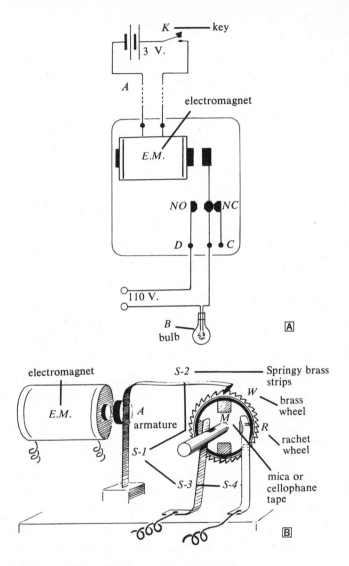

Fig. 62 Two simple wired relays

magnet, and *A* is its soft-iron armature. *S-1, S-2*, etc., indicate strips of light springy brass. *R* is a ratchet wheel which is rotated by the toothed end of *S-2*. On the side face of the brass wheel *W* small slips of mica, *M*, are glued (cellophane tape will serve) and the circuit between the two brushes *S-3* and *S-4* is alternately opened and closed as the wheel turns. A disadvantage of the device becomes obvious when the switched amperage is high. Make and break of a circuit should be very rapid to avoid spark or arc burning of the contacts. Here, the metal is subject to oxidation and the action is slow.

If the device is to be used for high-tension switching, it is hardly necessary to add that bare metal parts must be encased or insulated for safety.

## LIGHT-BEAM–CONTROLLED CIRCUITS

Apparatus of endless variety can be indirectly controlled by a light beam. Burglar alarms and light-operated devices such as self-opening doors are obvious applications of the light-operated relay. Although a fairly efficient relay can be constructed from an old solenoid and other pieces of scrap, the precision and neatness of the manufactured article are desirable in the circuits now described. One form is double-acting insofar as it closes two circuits simultaneously when the armature is attracted. This could sound a warning bell and at the same time light an electric bulb. The unit is intended to plug into an octal socket of the international tube type. The electro-magnet coil is of a 10-K. resistance, so that with as much as 50 volts applied the current consumption should not exceed 5 ma. The main contacts are rated to handle up to 2 amp. at 110 volts. From beneath the octal base the eight contacts are numbered as shown in Fig. 63.

A wide range of photocells with differing functions is now obtainable, and although the best-quality units are fairly expensive, very efficient cheaper cells are on the market. In general one may say that the resistance of a photocell drops considerably when illuminated. Transistors exhibit this resistance change when either heat rays or the visible spectrum of light falls on the actual semiconducting region, and many experimenters have made effective photocells by scraping off the paint from old glass-protected transistors.

Of the manufactured transistors designed to be light-responsive, the GE-X6 with a gain of about 50 is typical, and these have the usual three tail connectors. However, cadmium sulfide cells are also popular with experimenters. These units, with only two tail wires, are light-dependent resistors, and they are both sensitive and cheap. Let us assume that one of this type has been acquired—for example (Clairey) CL905H.

A useful preliminary experiment consists in setting

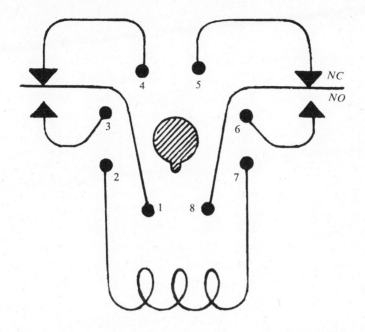

*Fig. 63 Relay base contacts*

up a simple relay loop containing such a photoconductive cadmium sulfide cell. As shown in the circuit of Fig. 64A, the cell $P$ is directly in series with the relay $RY$, the rheostat $R$, the battery $B$, and the switch $S$. A pressure of some 45 volts should be supplied by $B$; this may come from part of a high-tension battery (30 cells), or, provided one has already constructed the power supply unit of Chapter 10, an equivalent d.c. pressure may be tapped from this.

The resistance of the series loop can be altered by the rheostat $R$ (one side of a 1-megohm potentiom-

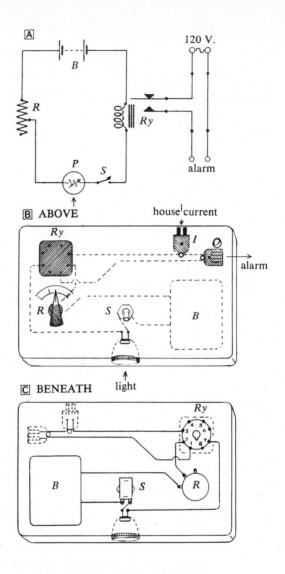

A

120 V.

B

R

Ry

P  S

alarm

B ABOVE

house current

Ry

I

alarm

R  S  B

C BENEATH  light

Ry

B  S  R

Fig. 64 Simple photo-relay

eter, and this serves to control the operating point; by means of it the degree of illumination of *P* needed to close the relay can be adjusted and a critical setting obtained.

Fix the photocell, which is button-shaped and about 1 cm. in diameter, in the base of a little enclosure such as the Bakelite cover of an old lamp socket so that light from the front affects it. Make sure that the tail wires are still insulated and mount the cell in a hole in the side of a container box. Devise a little shutter to cut off light from the cell as required. Fig. 64B shows a convenient arrangement of the box. Above the top panel are the relay, the rheostat control knob, the on-off switch, and the sockets for the house-current input and output. These connectors may be the usual 5-amp. flex junction pieces, but notice that the input socket must connect with the pin-projecting junction screwed to the panel. The other components— battery, rheostat, and wiring to the octal base of the relay—lie beneath the panel (Fig. 64C).

Attach the 110-volt output socket to some form of alarm, such as a red warning lamp or a fire-alarm bell. Illuminate the photocell with as much light as is intended to set off the alarm. Now, with this in action, increase the resistance *R* to the point where further increase causes the relay to open and cut off the alarm. Mark this setting of the control knob while the alarm is still operating. Darkening of the cell by passing the hand in front will, in this critical state, stop the alarm, whereas illumination will again close the relay and start it. Failure to extinguish could result from light from the alarm bulb itself shining on the photocell.

In bright light the resistance of the cell may drop to under 100 ohm, but in total darkness it will rise again to perhaps 10 million ohm so that even if left switched on the current consumption is under $\frac{1}{200}$ ma. Care should be taken not to overload the relay contacts, which may be designed to carry only 2 amp. If a big amperage is needed to energize the final alarm device, a second relay with more heavily built contacts can be operated by the initial one. A homemade relay with heavy contacts capable of handling 6 amp. may well be actuated by the small 2-amp. manufactured relay. This would apply in the case of the burglar alarm described below.

## AN ELECTROMAGNETIC ALARM

An alarming noisemaker was built up by the writer making use of a manufactured solenoid, but even with a homemade coil the construction should be obvious from Fig. 65. It operates on the normal a.c. house-current voltage and is somewhat massive, but little ingenuity is needed to scale down the whole and run it on a 12-volt supply.

A solenoid, *A*, of 500 turns of A.W.G. 18 wire is

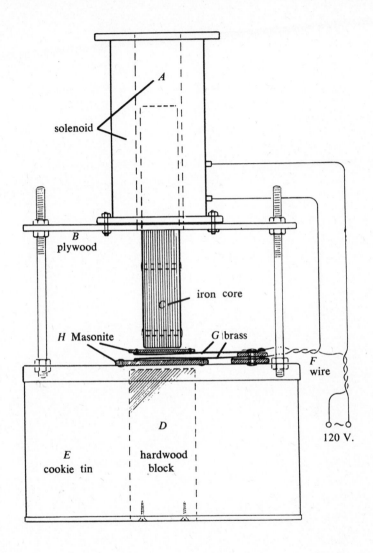

Fig. 65 The alarming noisemaker

wound on 1½-in. square-section tube of cardboard 5½ in. long. This is screwed to a piece of plywood, *B*, the same size as the lid of a 9-in. cookie tin, *E*, which acts as a drum. The lid is bolted to the corners of the plywood with four 6-in. lengths of $\frac{5}{16}$-in. threaded rod, as shown in the diagram. A laminated core of iron strips, *C*, riveted together, forms a massive 1¼-in. bar about 7½ in. long and weighing some 3 lb. A 4-in. square of Masonite, *H*, is riveted to the middle of the lid in order to spread the blow given by the iron bar when it drops.

Next, a simple switch consisting of two springy brass strips, *G*, ½ in. wide by about 6 in. long is made. A piece of Masonite one quarter the length of the strips is sandwiched between them at one end. This end is insulated from the lid with a thin piece of Masonite and is fastened to the top of the lid just inside one of the pieces of supporting rod. The top strip of brass must also be insulated from the iron core with Masonite. Flexible wire is soldered to the two brass strips. Inside the tin a block of hardwood, *D*, constitutes an anvil struck by the tin lid when the iron bar falls.

It is not difficult to imagine the effect of closing the external electric switch, since the action is similar to that of an electric bell. The core jumps up into the strongest part of the solenoid field, thereby opening the contact springs beneath. Dropping back again, it remakes the circuit. The repetition, it must be admitted, is not very rhythmic, but the racket is astonishing. Occasionally the iron core is hurled right out of the solenoid, suggesting that a stop, or an upper gong, is needed. No doubt the cookie tin inverted over the solenoid and clamped by the studding so that its base forms an upper stop would result in an even more fearsome din. Sparking at the contact strips, which is considerable, might well be reduced by a capacitor across them.

The current is limited by the high inductance of the coil with its iron core inside, so that a 10-amp. fuse is sufficient to protect the wiring. Junior constructors of this model must be given the normal and important warning of danger from any inadequate insulation of the electric supply.

## TRANSISTORIZED ALARMS

One of the simpler arrangements for operating a relay (with a much smaller battery supply than 45 volts) employs the amplifying effect of a transistor of the p-n-p type (GE-2 PNP). Fig. 66 shows such a circuit which is economical of current and is sensitive. The resistance of the photocell $P$ drops with the incidence of light. This increases the flow of base current through the transistor $Tr$, and the gain of $Tr$ then allows enough emitter or output current to flow and operate the relay $Ry$.

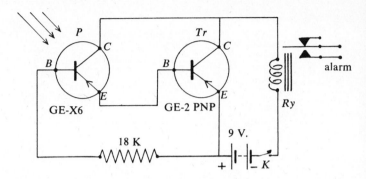

*Fig. 66 Light-operated alarm*

At this stage it should be possible to leave details of component layout to the ingenuity of the reader, and therefore only the circuitry is suggested.

The further alarm arrangement now described is quite diminutive, being in fact mounted on a 1½-in. square of insulator. It makes use of an oscillator-type circuit, the action of which is stopped by increase in resistance of the photocell.

Fig. 67 shows one of many possible oscillator arrangements which would produce a warning note in the speaker *S*. The drawing is arranged to clarify this action. *T* is an ordinary push-pull audio transformer with a split primary. Its output coil is of low resistance (about 0.3 ohm), and the winding of the speaker *S* is also of low value. Examine first the heavy line wiring of Fig. 67. It shows part of the primary winding, together with the 1-mfd. capacitor, forming an oscillatory loop taking power from the battery *F*, and joined to the collector and emitter of the transistor *A*.

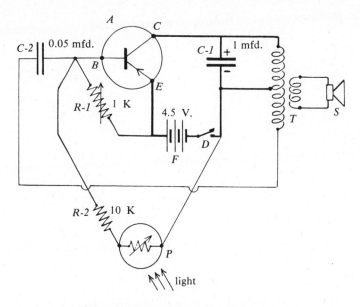

*Fig. 67 Light-operated oscillator*

The rest of the transformer winding constitutes a feedback coil injecting small fluctuations into the base circuit of *A* and so maintaining the oscillations.

Now look at the loop drawn with oblique lines joining the resistors to the photocell and battery. The 10 K. is just a limiting resistor which prevents too large a current from reaching *A* should resistance of *P* fall too low. If the resistance of *P* falls, as it does with light, then more base current will flow; alternatively we may think of *B* becoming more negative relative to *E*. The usual amplifying action of the transistor will therefore ensue. Oscillation will start up when the photocell is illuminated and cease in darkness.

An arrangement perhaps more usual in light-actuated systems is that in which the device goes into operation when light is cut off from the photocell. Thus a shadow interrupting a beam may result in the opening of a door, ringing of an alarm, and so on. Only minor circuit changes are needed to reverse the action of the system here described.

It may be helpful to list actual components used in the circuit of Fig. 67.

| | |
|---|---|
| *A* | GE-2 PNP transistor. Gain—70. Maximum current—250 ma. $B$ = base, $C$ = collector, $E$ = emitter) |
| *F* | 4.5-volt battery (disconnected by alligator clips $D$) |
| *C-1* | 1-mfd. subminiature electrolytic capacitor |
| *C-2* | 0.05-mfd. capacitor |
| *R-1* | 1-K. preset control rheostat (radio spares) |
| *R-2* | 10-K. resistor (brown, black, orange, silver) |
| *S* | Miniature speaker (3-ohm coil) |
| *T* | Push-pull transformer. TT 46 (Repanco) with center-tapped primary and 0.3-ohm output coil |
| *P* | Photoconductive cell CL905H (Clairex) |

The whole unit is contained in a small polystyrene box. Compactness is aided by fitting leads of the transistor *A* and the cell *P* into the tiny plastic sockets now available for the purpose; these also allow easy interchange of components without unsoldering. The photocell fits into one end of a hole, blackened internally, bored through a cork. This black-painted tunnel only allows light from a limited source to reach and actuate the cell. The light intensity operating point is controlled by the setting of the rheostat *R-1*.

It is fascinating to try for yourself the effect of different light intensities and also to investigate color filters, which allow only a limited range of wave lengths to fall on the cell. Experimenters who actually set up and play with circuits containing an electric eye quickly come to realize their vast potentialities. Sensitive light-operated circuits are a feature of modern automation and have become widespread in factories for the purposes of counting and controlling products. Grading and automatic rejection of faulty items can be done mechanically at high speed by controlled relay action. The relay which will switch on lamps and alarms will obviously start and stop motors equally well, and you may find a really interesting field to explore in the control of relays by radio frequency.

Minute, lightweight relays and motors are sold for incorporation in model aircraft and boats. Where weight is a consideration, experimenters may prefer to use power transistors as "on-off" switches, since these, with appropriate circuitry, can replace electromagnetic relays for operating motors.

*Appendix* THE IDENTIFICATION
OF RESISTOR VALUES

The ohmic value of a resistor is identified by a color code because resistors may be very tiny though their number of ohms is large, and because colors are less likely to be erased by wear than a printed number. Even so, overheating sometimes makes color recognition difficult when some shades tend to brown.

In the commonly used system of color marking, colored bands are read from the one nearest the end. The meanings of the colors are given below. The first color is the first digit, the second color is the next digit, and the third color is the power of ten of the multiplier—that is, the number of zeros following the first two figures. This holds true through blue (for which add six zeros). However, purple, gray, and white are not used in the third band. Silver in the third band means the multiplier is $10^{-2}$ (divide by 100) and gold in the third band means $10^{-1}$ (divide by 10).

If marked, the fourth band states the accuracy or tolerance that may be expected. Gold means $\pm 5\%$ and silver means $\pm 10\%$. Those not marked may be $\pm 20\%$ of the stated value.

| *Code* | | |
|---|---|---|
| | BLACK | 0 |
| | BROWN | 1 |
| | RED | 2 |
| | ORANGE | 3 |
| | YELLOW | 4 |
| | GREEN | 5 |
| | BLUE | 6 |
| | PURPLE | 7 |
| | GRAY | 8 |
| | WHITE | 9 |

As the colors are largely in the spectral sequence, they are, with a little practice, quickly memorized and the values of resistors recognized. Study of the following examples should make the use of the system quite clear.

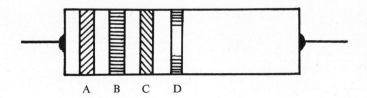

A  B  C  D

Band A *Red*
  B *Purple*
  C *Brown* $= 270$ ohms $\pm 10\%$
  D *Silver*

Band A *Brown*
  B *Green*
  C *Blue* $= 15$ megohms $\pm 5\%$
  D *Gold*

# INDEX

# INDEX

*About the Author*

The son of an instrument maker, Alan Bulman has been familiar with tools and model making since boyhood. Born in Newcastle-upon-Tyne, England, Mr. Bulman received a B.Sc., an M.Sc., and an Education degree from Durham University.

For many years he taught science and art and architecture in a school in South Wales. He is an Associate of the Institute of Physics and the Physical Society, and since 1949 has been head of the Physics Department at the Cambridgeshire High School for Boys in England.

Mr. Bulman is an enthusiastic watercolorist. His pictures have been exhibited at the Royal Society of British Artists and at several provincial galleries. He is also deeply interested in orchestral music and has played the violin with the Cambridge Philharmonic for many years.